CLACKAMAS LITERARY REVIEW

2020
Volume XXIV

Clackamas Community College
Oregon City, Oregon

CLACKAMAS LITERARY REVIEW

Managing Editor
Matthew Warren

Associate Editors

Tim Cook	Jennifer Davis	Jack Eikrem
Delilah Martinez	Ali Noman	Nicole Rosevear
Alicia Schmidt	Jenelle Vader	Amy Warren

Assistant Editors & Designers

Alice G. Bjornstedt	Dylan Croonquist	Lauren Eagles
Nicholas A. Englehardt	Eli Eshelman	Megan Flohr
Bethany Graves	Edan James-Wadsworth	Daman McConnell
Michelle Moore	Isabella Renner	Dariyon Risberg
Jordan Runyen	Sophie Schmidt	Hannah Spahr

Cover Art
Healing Hands by Sophie Estrada

The *Clackamas Literary Review* is published annually at Clackamas Community College. Manuscripts are read from September 1st to December 31st. By submitting your work to *CLR*, you indicate your consent for us to publish accepted work in print and online. Issues I–XI are available through our website; issues XII–XXIII are available on our Submittable, and through your favorite online bookseller.

Clackamas Literary Review
19600 Molalla Avenue, Oregon City, Oregon 97045
ISBN: 978-1-7320333-2-0
Printed by Lightning Source
www.clackamasliteraryreview.org

Acknowledgments

Special thanks to Ooligan Press and the Write to Publish writing contest for partnering with our magazine to publish its 2020 poetry award recipient. We're proud to be part of this amazing opportunity and experience for writers and poets.

CONTENTS

PROSE

POSSIBILITY

CONTRIBUTORS

Editors' Note

Memories: they are fragments we collect throughout our lives. We cherish them and we scorn them. When called to mind, they can cause delight or repulsion, sorrow or joy. Poets and writers choose to gather those memories, whether elegant pieces or searing scraps, then carefully reshape them into artifacts to be admired, offering the opportunity for the reader to hold and feel a time and a place that was not theirs. Some more elegant or composed, some raw or emotional, each poem, each story, offers value and perspective to its readers.

The creators have chosen to share such stories with us—the editors of the *Clackamas Literary Review*—so that we might read and know their memories. Editors spent many weeks reading and discussing works to accept or reject. Many challenged us, creating discussions and arguments that helped us shape and produce this collection.

We tempered wording without shattering the creator's intent. We arranged each work carefully, setting pieces next to their complements, to evoke the deepest emotion from this collection. This collaboration between author and publisher is one you now hold in your hands. May this volume give you, the reader, a glimpse into the memories that others lived and have chosen to share.

Downpour

Lisa Higgs

A break in rain, which fell steady all night,
leaves the woodpecker to fill lack with echo,
perfect rhythm beaten into branches swollen
green. One dart of dawn birds scatters droplets,
gentle cascade of wings. I wipe the page
dry of morning, wait for something unknown
to be made clear. As if between rain-bands
reason is ever-present, cloud-held, ready
to wash what's past in downpour, or drown
futures in lush sodden lawns. Yet instinct
says what is one thing will soon be another.
I have found no way to avoid this thought,
which rattles me from sleep some nights in shocks
of light, cracking to earth as pulse of sky.

How Things End

Joel Savishinsky

How do things end?

The expectant, resonant chord
bringing to a close
a Renaissance dance.

The slowed roll of
the stroller being
stored in the attic.

The halting wake of
a patient's walker.

High tides and daylight
drawing down
the dreams of the moon.

The studied way
your eyes no longer
meet mine.

The recession
of a pulse.

Six Months after the Divorce

Adam Tavel

My parents didn't want their jeans to touch,
standing on a narrow crooked pier beside
Schoolhouse Pond in October wind, their hands
clutching a spool they couldn't reel back in.

For months my sister begged to fly her kite,
a Christmas gift, its grinning Care Bear perched
askew in dust above her certain rod,
the streamer pocked with bite marks from her rage

when she prowled time-outs for things to wreck.
At last it soared a hundred feet above
our heads, banking hard right, one spreader gone,
the bear a headless belly flapping like

a grocery bag sucked to a box fan's cage.
I decided on my bench to hate them all
and turned away to watch an overcoat
toss tattered clumps of bread to ducks that left

as quickly as they came in rippling glides
like carvings of themselves, expressionless
and still, their heads too green to be believed.
Beyond the sloping bank my mother's car

purred where soon we'd swap our weekend clothes
from trunk to rusted trunk and warm ourselves
by sitting on our palms—a dull exchange
then fifteen minutes overdue. I heard

the snap before the shriek and turned to spot
a fluttered diamond shrink against the sky
so fast it seemed it never was at all,
as if the distant sun-blanched pines were all

we came to see, as long as we ignored
the broken bitter weeping of a girl
and looping leminscates of string that fell,
a silver hair cascading down the rail.

What Happened Then

Chris Anderson

I miss the way I felt when I was
taking Prednisone. I was like a cloud,
observing the sky. I shone.
When Andy took it, during chemo,

he said it made him feel like he could
leap tall buildings
with a single bound—and that he *must*
leap tall buildings

with a single bound. O, how I miss
Andy, too, and the alder
and the fern, and the light
on the water—the way I felt when

I touched the trunk of that tree—
what happened then.

Meet Me at Register Five

Michelle DeLiso

I stood in ShopRite's condiment aisle one summer morning two years ago, scanning the shelves for sugar-free salad dressing and thought, I hate grocery shopping.

Every week it's the same drill: Load the shopping cart, find the shortest checkout line, empty the cart's contents onto the conveyor belt, pack my own reusable grocery bags, shove the bags into my decade-old Honda Pilot, unload the bags back home, and stock the kitchen amid questions from my husband and two kids: *Didn't they have blueberry yogurt? Why did you buy grapes? You forgot tissues?* (For years, I'd harbored this question: Why don't you guys get the groceries and I'll interrogate YOU when you get home? At some point I'd started saying it out loud.)

Standing blankly in the condiment aisle, a wave of defeat washed over me.

I yanked my glasses off and pulled a bottle of Italian dressing so close to my face I could feel my breath on it. It's the only way I can read the nutrient label.

"Hello, Miss."

A kind, familiar voice I hadn't heard in ages sliced through my apathy. It was Nazrahi, the cashier who used to work on register five. I hadn't seen him for months. I had assumed he was long gone, and he had taken the last ounce of joy I felt at the grocery store with him.

Before I met Nazrahi, I'd been an impatient shopper, incensed by customers who blocked the aisles gossiping with neighbors and who later stalled the checkout line. Couldn't they see that my Popsicles were melting on the conveyor belt while they carried on with the cashier?

By contrast, I was a checkout line rock star: I never delayed fellow shoppers. I never quibbled with the cashier over alleged markdowns. My coupons were always valid, and I placed each one atop its corresponding product. I practically packed my items faster than the cashier could scan them.

But I only impressed myself. Until I met Nazrahi.

Nazrahi worked at the new ShopRite in my neighborhood. Register five quietly mocked customers like me, because it bordered a series of express lanes. Dizzied by the store's unfamiliar layout, I couldn't figure out where register five fit. I wasn't about to be the fool who unloaded a week's worth of groceries in an express lane.

"Is this lane only for orders of twelve items or less?" I'd finally asked Nazrahi, the cashier at register five, a few weeks after I'd started shopping there.

"I take all orders, Miss. Come on down," he said. He sounded like a game show host.

I unloaded my haul, displayed my coupons, and tossed my canvas bags toward the bagging area.

"You're a great shopper," Nazrahi said. "Everything is in order."

I nodded and felt my cheeks go warm. All I'd wanted was to get out of the store. But now this kind stranger was making small talk.

A thirty-something brunette behind me mumbled to herself, but I heard every word:

"Unbelievable, bringing this huge order to the express line."

My heart thumped with anger. Kill her with kindness, or throw my iceberg lettuce at her head?

"Good morning," Nazrahi chirped, shattering my dilemma. "Do you see those four registers?" He motioned to the four miniature conveyor belts. "Those are express. They'll be happy to help if you are in a hurry. This line—never express."

I couldn't help myself—I smirked at the brunette. I paid and, eager to finish, simply thanked Nazrahi. After that, I became a regular on his line.

"There she is, my best customer," he'd say, beaming at me each week. "Did you find everything you needed? Any coupons today?"

While he scanned and I bagged, we'd continue the previous week's chat. *Did your husband like the new almond milk? I'm glad your son is feeling better. What did you cook for the holiday? Now that your kids are getting older, will you go back to work?*

In bits and pieces, he came to know my story, and I came to know his. He was from Nigeria, but his family, as he described it, had been "kicked out." They'd lived in Italy for a short time, then came to the United States. I don't know whether his family arrived as immigrants or as refugees, and I wasn't sure if he had children. Somehow those questions always felt too personal to ask.

"Are you happy in this country?" I asked him instead.

"Yes, very happy," he said. "We are so lucky, Miss. I like this job and this beautiful store. It's good for customers and for me." The register pinged as he scanned. "I keep meaning to ask your nationality. I can't figure it out."

I considered his question for a moment. It would be so easy to say "American," but there was more to my story, too.

"I was born in New Jersey," I finally said, "but I have family from Puerto Rico and a few other places."

As I waited for the card reader to process my payment, the barrel-chested man in line behind me checked his watch and sighed.

The checkout line rock star in me wanted to skedaddle to give the man his turn. But during the short time I had gotten to know Nazrahi, he had reminded me that connecting with the folks we see as we drudge through our routines was more important than rushing toward the exit.

"What are the other places?" Nazrahi asked, handing me my receipt.

"Italy and Algeria."

"Oh, that's an interesting mix."

The man behind me inched closer and held out his loyalty card for Nazrahi, who gave me a knowing look.

"Have a good day," I told him. I gave him a thumbs up. "We'll talk next week."

"Next time we'll talk food," Nazrahi said. "I want to know what kind of Puerto Rican food you cook."

Except that conversation never happened. Just like that, Nazrahi vanished. He must have taken a week's vacation, I thought. When two weeks became three, I started to worry. I changed my shopping routine, even swung by on a few evenings in case his shift had changed. But he was nowhere to be found.

One idle Monday morning at the store, more than a month after I'd last seen Nazrahi, another cashier, a redhead with a voice like Rosanne Barr, shouted across two lanes to her coworker as I searched for an open register: "The paper bags run out because Nazrahi isn't here. He's the only one who restocks them on morning shift."

I lingered at a candy rack feigning interest in Tic Tacs, hoping she'd say more. When she didn't, I decided to pay at her register and ask about him. I rehearsed innocuous questions in my head as I emptied my cart: *Is Nazrahi on a long vacation? Was Nazrahi transferred to another store?* I'd even invented a lie because I didn't want her to think I was a stalker: *Say, there was a cashier who was going to give me a recipe. His name is Nazrahi. Do you know when he works?*

The redheaded cashier was bubbly in a self-deprecating way. She joked about not slamming my laundry detergent on top of my eggs and said she wanted to inhale my crumb cake. I couldn't find an opening for my burning question in what sounded like her stand-up comedy routine. I'd blown it.

Deep down, I'd been afraid of the answer.

So when I heard Nazrahi's voice again as I stood in the condiment aisle months after he'd vanished, I nearly gouged an eye shoving my glasses back on.

"Nazrahi! Where have you been?"

Even as I spoke, regret twisted my gut. A filmy gaze had replaced the expectant glean in his eyes. He shambled toward me with a woman who appeared to be his wife.

"I have been away from work," he said simply, his voice cracking. He glanced down the aisle at no one, then turned to the woman, who was supporting him with one arm. "My wife is helping me with the sickness."

What sickness? I'd wanted to ask, but the question seemed too intrusive. Whatever it was, it had made him frail. It had to be serious. A lump loomed in my throat.

"I'm sorry you're not feeling well," I whispered. I swallowed hard and turned to his wife. "You are so lucky. Nazrahi is a hard worker and very nice man."

She grasped his hand tighter.

"Thank you, dear," she said, touching my shoulder.

I willed her to say more, but she turned to Nazrahi and stayed quiet.

"Very good to see you, Miss," Nazrahi said after a long moment. "We must finish the shopping now."

"Okay," I said. All my energy was focused on bridling tears. "You have a good day, and I'll pray that you feel better soon."

Nazrahi and his wife thanked me and shuffled away.

Wait! I wanted to call out. *Don't go. When will you come back to work?*

Will I ever see you again?

But this wasn't a movie. There was no happy reckoning before the closing credits. I said nothing as they picked up a jar of olives and tottered out of sight.

A cart rattled past me, and a customer huffed.

I'd been blocking the aisle.

For weeks I vainly scanned the checkout lanes for Nazrahi's raven hair and breezy smile, hoping he'd emerge from behind a sale rack and say, *There she is, my best customer.*

Sometimes I'd imagine what he might have said to the harried customers who reminded me of the shopper I used to be before I'd met him: *It's a beautiful morning! Tell me something good!* Once, as I waited in a stalled checkout line, I laughed, remembering an encounter Nazrahi once had with an extreme couponer who'd been ahead of me in line. The conveyor belt was heaped with what had to be thirty bottles of body wash:

"Miss, did you see that stack of coupons?" he'd asked me, leaning theatrically over the conveyor belt. "I thought my register would explode! Who needs that much body wash?"

Now, I toss broccoli crowns and salmon fillets into my cart every week, but I feel bereft despite the bounty. I haven't seen my kind stranger in two years, and still, I search for him every time I shop. I wish I could tell him that my older son got his driver's license, and that I learned how to cook Korean beef bulgogi using the shaved steak I found in the meat department. I wish the questions swirling inside my head weren't so personal, or I'd pull that redheaded cashier aside and ask:

Why was Nazrahi sick? How is his wife? Do they have children who take care of them?

And, who restocks the paper bags now?

Because Sometimes It Is All We Can Do

—after Naomi Shihab Nye

Suzy Harris

We must bless ourselves with peaches,
not be too quick to wash the sticky juice
from hands and face.

We must bless ourselves with falling leaves,
ones that drift before landfall,
that carry with them a stolen glance.

We must bless ourselves with apples,
the wormy ones too high in the tree
for the fruit-picker, too high for a ladder.

We must bless ourselves with early September light
that dances and shimmers,
and with darkness that comes before we are ready,

with gentle wind that carries the scent of rain and mud.
We must bless ourselves with forgiveness,
now, when it is not too late.

Interning

John Struloeff

Amid the grief from my mother's death,
I noticed that in the condolence messages
people kept saying she was being *interned*
instead of *interred*. To them, no difference.
To me, who was taught by my mother
to care about the choice and formation
of words, I was irritated by the lack
of concern about the language of her death.
She did not birth me to become a professor
of words, but I became one, and this alighted
a part of her spirit that had long been
shadowed and abandoned. She sent me
empty crosswords and completed crosswords,
news clippings with misspellings circled
in her blue pen, and poems she'd written
for every key turning point of my life.
She was being *interred* on Saturday, by God.
But then, because I am never finished
with words, I began to think of her *interning*,
as one of my students would during summer break.
Well, she'd waited eighty-four years for this break.

And interning for whom? For God? In the land
of the spirit? She'd waited so long to not be able
to do so many things. She had mused for me
about the jobs she'd never had, the books
she'd never written, on many quiet evenings
after she'd grown old and I had begun
what she called *my adventures*. The mother
of six children, the wife of an Old World man,
she told me she was living *vicariously* through me.
Which city in which part of the world
would we visit next? Moscow? Stratford
upon Avon? Bethlehem? I showed her photos
upon my return of our adventures. She glowed.
Yet through all those years, all those cities,
I never thought I would be interning vicariously
through her, now, in a land I can't even imagine.

Pomegranates

Jack Eikrem

in granada they bloom for us
fruited munitions
shrapnel
as sharp as november mornings
and bitter as corked-tainted wine
     i know
         the tree of your body could never wither
         while you are still green
we eat
pomegranates on the terrace and pretend
to have a view of the alhambra
it is cool here at evening
the sky
is the color of a fresh wound
and the cathedral bell
sings of things the world
forgot
     you crucify me
     with a kiss
     stigmatize my wrists
     transubstantiate liminal dust

we rehearse

death

in place of absolution

and the surgeons

who open

your back to steal your spine

find

seedlets lodged in your pulp

and probe until

everything changes

sever

this fruit

with a sword of divisions

hold

the bright halves under

water

till the arils sink to the bottom

The Vigil

Rachel Arteaga

It was difficult to believe that he was gone, that his full-hearted voice would never call out its bright "hello!" in their doorways again. The men stared out from their front porches, withdrawn and silent. The women settled it into their bones. They knew that the quiet that had fallen over their households in the weeks after the accident would slowly be replaced by the sounds of the day and its many and constant demands.

On those mornings, the children would wake to traverse the distance in their fathers' eyes. They pulled their fathers away from their grief and into the pressing moment: the hometown baseball game, the playground swing, the bleeding cut from a careless fall. The women soothed and watched and waited. It mattered greatly to them that his wife had outlived him, that she was now among them, alone, outside of the tall fences of her husband's encircling arms. The widowing day had come for her first, and quickly. The children were all very young; the women hungry; the men still strong.

One by one the men had mentioned her, in furtive moments of concern. A gesture of the hand toward the house at the end of the road, half-empty and in shadow. A decision, spur-sharp, to check in on things down that way, to see if anything was needed. Without much thought, they'd stood to stride away from their own homes to visit her, hands aching to be worked down to the living bone. Their minds searching for reprieve from their self-reference, and for a way to keep in some small way their friend—a man who would have done for any one of them what they were doing now, and more. After all, she was there alone, and could probably use a hand.

She had never been able to have children. Her childlessness was like a broken sparrow's wing and song; it circled downward from the sky, its notes repeated and unchanging over all the many years. Nothing could be said or done. There simply were no children among all of the other children, and in the house, the sound of their absence echoed from the pale and perfect walls. Her husband would have been a wonderful father. He was adored by all of the children there, and as they grew, they, like their fathers, came to admire him. But she was distant. It's true that she had always asked the women about their sons and daughters by their names, sent gifts, remembered birthdays. But even with the early mornings spent in her flowering gardens and orchards, the rough work of cutting back dead leaves and branches, her hands seemed empty and unaccounted for. She was regarded with pity, for the emptiness, and with suspicion, for the rest. She knew this, and kept apart.

It was in this habit of solitude that she came to be alone in the house on the night of the vigil held in remembrance of her husband. The women had organized the memorial and had considered every detail. Votive candles were rummaged for in attics and in closets, drawers and shelving; paper holders were gathered and unfolded, so thin and fragile they could have floated outward on the water, if there had been a lake nearby. In silence, the walk began, as every family made its way in line toward the house and then encircled it. As the sun set, every person lit a candle, mothers and fathers striking matches for the youngest among them. It was important for everyone to attend, and for everyone to see. As night fell, the darkness never fully came, so bright were all the candlewicks. The flames were beautiful as they did their work. The shingles were dry and caught quickly. The smoke rose into the sky. The house burned through the night.

In the morning, the children ran and played in the ashes. The men withdrew. The women soothed and watched and waited.

Planets Don't Talk About Their Feelings

Winner, 2020 Ooligan Press Write to Publish contest in poetry

Erin Doyle

I thought the planet Neptune was powerful,
blue and heavenly.
The Sun still leashes it up
and walks it like a dog.

Tonight, an unfamiliar earring on your nightstand
stops me in my tracks.
I say nothing,
I crawl into your bed.

While you snore,
moonlight colors me blue.
I can't sleep,
I roll over,
I wrap my arms around you.

Your Lilacs Nest in Me

And your very flesh shall be a great poem.

—Walt Whitman

Darcy Smith

I give you a constant breath behind the door.
I give rusted hinges, unsprung locks.
I give you my sprig of lilac.
I give you wet smoke.
I give you the earth breached.
I give you endless, hopeful, airless heat.
I give you the sickle moon inside this ache.

Let me lay this sprig of lilac at your feet.
Let me in the spider's web. Let me stick
to the center of forever spinning pouring
my hair falling from a branch, from a willow's arms
I give a song, myself. I give you the want,
the ache, the gnawing need to be
the woods that listened you.

Let me receive you lounging on my windowsill
your long-lit stanzas cascading air
strung like the taut of summer before a rain.

Let me pluck a mint leaf. Let me be your morning
tea. Let me hide inside the rim. Let me sip the silver
edge of empty but for your mud slicked evenings,
for your tumbled sighs, for in the stranger's face
in his eyes, in shoulders cresting, in arms glistening
in each shattered second, a stifled gaze.

Come now, William you must see
Vincent born in you. It's just a book, see how his oils
birth and sing and bind you in ribbons torn
from within. Let me show you his blue studies.

Let me warm your tea. Let me set you inside
my cup. Let me open the nests that Vincent made,
hidden in this book I use to cover water stains, cover
sickled cold, cover the soft pine nicks of my father's table.

Take my sprig of lilac. Take my blistered cries
my cheap whiskey, my want of what is not written, scenes
unseen sweat, piling in stacks of air-dried words like oils
mixed in me, speaking as Van Gogh does screaming
in my ear, his severed galaxies inside my mouth, as if
he speaks only motion, as if you speak me inside
his needled light, inside his cell, inside San Remy,
inside my thinning silence, inside his cypress.

For want of nature, he brought birds nests in
the hollow of night, he was twigs breathing, he was
saliva from a robin's breast. The spider silk he threw

a knotty white, one tone pulsing on moss drying,
on glinted black the brambles he snapped
the wind, black bars wobbled my throat, you warbled
me into his star spun sea into your trailing phrases into
hayfields into nights starred into unmetered longing
my eyes scalded for want of an iris opened, for want
of one true line, for the spell his nests cast
on my every broken branch. Keep my sprig of lilac.

Lily

Paulann Petersen

Drops flung
from a goddess' breast
formed the Milky Way—
a strew of countless
creamy stars. A few escaped
the sky's reach, falling
into the world. Where each
touched down,
it bloomed.

These white stars
learned to call earth
their home. Her fallen milk,
they ooze her perfume—
sweet and thick.
An incense stolen
from the sky's own
alchemist of scent.

Call It Love

Bruce Barrow

Sally was 60 and mostly accepted it. Acceptance, she told me over coffee a few weeks after we met, was a choice. If I hadn't come to that understanding already, she said, I could thank her for the insight now or later, but not with flowers, because she could pick those herself from her neighbors' yards after it got dark. Dinner out would be her preference, if I was looking for a good way to say thank you, but again, up to me. Just don't forget.

"Of course," I said. "I'll let you know."

"And preferably soon," she added. "I've also accepted that time is short." She said this with a smile and a wink, first her left eye and then her right, because it delighted her that she could wink either one, something she'd only mastered in the past couple of months. Did it watching herself on her iPhone while she was on conference calls at her desk. She was a CPA and liked to remind me that by 60 she'd heard it all, so indulged herself when she could. It was a lesson she wished she'd understood sooner because, even as an accountant, she couldn't begin to add up how many other tricks she'd lost the opportunity to learn.

"So maybe you shouldn't be an accountant," I ventured. "Not that I'm remarking on your ability to count or not."

She winked twice and blew me a kiss.

Nearly every morning before work we had coffee together at the bakery across from our office and this was usually how it went. Sally liked an audience and I liked Sally. She was fourteen years older than me, which meant nothing as far as I was concerned, but I could rarely get her to go out with me. A special occasion, or more accurately, my creation of one—'Accountant's Day ', 'Underappreciated Accountant's Day', 'That Rare Special Day after Accountant's Day'—seemed to win me the most dates, but even then only when there was some unidentifiable magic in the air. Just as often I'd get a smile, an air kiss and a 'maybe next time.'

Both of us were divorced, Sally twice, both times her choice. "Men are bastards," she said shortly after we'd fallen into our morning coffee routine. "57% of them on any given day, climbing to a median 71% on football Sundays. I can show you the math."

"No need. I know your credentials."

"You'd be surprised how many don't." She gave me a hard look to punctuate this thought. Then she went silent and didn't say anything again until we'd crossed the street and were ready to queue for our different elevators and I figured there'd be a quick goodbye and that would be it. Instead she gave me a mischievous smile and touched my shoulder with her fingers, a tenderness so quick I could only appreciate it after it passed. "Nothing personal back there," she said, raising her voice to carry over the commotion in the lobby. "I didn't mean you. Coffee tomorrow?" Then she touched my shoulder again and disappeared into the crowd.

That was a year ago, an easy 400 cups of coffee between us since. There have also been two plays, one concert, a movie, a museum, two brunches and nine dinners, including those on concert or play nights. She's come home with me twice and invited me to her place once, where she warned me about the fallacy of sunk costs.

"I'm University of Chicago," I reminded her. "I get it."

"I'm not sure that you do," she said.

I laughed but it turns out she that meant it. For the next two weeks she skipped our morning coffee to make her point. That I showed up frustrated and worried every morning to wait for her meant something had been proved, so when she reappeared on the Monday of the third week I made my case.

"Sunk costs have nothing to do with it," I said. "I'm crazy about you, Sally. I don't want you to think there's something wrong or fake about that. I was here every day, even though you ignored my texts." I hoped I hadn't said too much but that I'd at least said enough. It was past time to admit the obvious, or to get it out in the open anyway, so Sally would know I'd finally caught up with her and understood what she'd certainly known all along—that she'd captured my heart, whether she wanted it or not.

She didn't answer right away, which unsettled me. Instead she stirred her cappuccino then sat back in her chair with her legs crossed and put her hands on her lap. She gave me a long steady look I couldn't interpret. Finally she spoke. "Steve. I'm more than fond of you. I'll give you credit for knowing that. You're a sweet, gentle soul and it's a pleasure spending time with you. And maybe best of all you know how to make me laugh. But..." She paused, eyes still on me, and an awkward twitch of a smile crossed her lips.

"But..." I echoed. "I kind of figured."

"No. You haven't figured at all." Then she smiled, not an accidental smile, but still a smile I wasn't sure I liked. She said, "I think maybe today is a good day to skip work."

Then she stood and picked up her purse. She was out of the door in a second and moving so fast I had to look both ways to find her. Just like every third woman in that part of the city at that time of morning she was wearing running shoes with her business clothes and she wasn't slowing down. With her shoulder length gray hair and maroon jacket, though, she was easy to follow, even though I didn't seem to be catching up. She looked back once, spotted me and gave me a wink, then just kept going. She had an eye for the gaps in the crowd and caught all the lights, or was close enough to catching them so that her pace never slowed. After following her for what might have been ten minutes or could have been twenty I was sweating and breathing hard, wishing I hadn't slacked at the gym, and she was still a block ahead of me, still weaving through the crowd, which was finally thinning.

She was easier to follow and I thought about yelling for her to wait up—I'd thought about that several times before—but didn't have the breath for it or couldn't overcome the sense that she wouldn't want me to attract more attention to us than our fast pace already had, if it had, which it probably hadn't. Since my goal was just to keep sight of her and keep up I wasn't paying attention to where we were, but now that she was easier to follow I looked around and saw buildings I didn't recognize—not office buildings but rough-looking apartments and narrow shops still shuttered from the night before. Graffiti and stunted trees in squares of dirt. There was almost no one on the street and a block ahead of me Sally stopped walking. I stopped too. Then I took a deep breath as she turned towards me. She was far enough away that to my near-sighted eyes she was a barely recognizable blur. To say I was baffled and worried doesn't really capture it. I was mystified, felt a slipperiness like panic. We stood there looking at each other across the distance. Sally was waiting for me but I'd stopped where I was. Maybe I was thinking, maybe I wasn't. I didn't feel sure of anything, and I didn't like it. I like order and reason, and this was neither, was at the other end of the scale. Still, I'd followed her. It made no sense to stop now. I don't know how long I stood there but it could have been minutes—two, five, even ten—while I tried to sort this moment out.

Then in a blurry motion Sally lifted her arm and my phone rang. I answered.

"Steve," Sally said. "What are you doing back there?"

"I'm not sure. Thinking," I said.

"This is the wrong neighborhood for that. Hurry up."

"Why? Where are we going? And why are we here?"

"I'm going to show you. I didn't think I wanted to, or that I should, but now I do."

"That's pretty cryptic."

"I'm a woman of mystery. It's the heart of my charm."

"Right," I said. "That's exactly how I would put it."

"The saddest surprise is no surprise at all. Somebody said that somewhere."

"That's probably true," I said. "In fact, I'm sure that it's true." I held the phone tight against my ear, as if hearing her voice would make her easier to see.

"So are you coming?" she asked.

"I think so," I said. "Give me a minute."

"The clock's ticking."

We stood looking at each other, our phones to our ears. Only the quiet from our respective ends of the street moving electronically between us. Then I lowered my phone and through my near-sightedness it appeared that Sally lowered hers. She stood with a wide stance, arms crossed as I walked towards her. The morning sun edged her height with a pale gold while the browns and grays of neglected buildings filled the space behind her. With each step I took she came more clearly into focus. White sneakers, creased gray slacks, maroon jacket and white blouse. Her gray shoulder-length hair pulled back in a pony-tail to show off her cheekbones. Brown eyes full of light. A sly, satisfied smile. I stopped three feet in front of her, but felt closer to her than I'd ever felt before.

"You made it," she said.

"I did." My heart was wrapped in her magic. I closed my eyes and leaned to meet her for a kiss but she didn't meet me. I opened my eyes.

She stood where she was and grinned at me. "You're just so sweet," she said. Then, with her grin softening into a smile that emp-tied me out, she took two steps backwards, turned and started walk-ing.

Love Note to Nye Beach

Dave Seter

I won't make fun of your castles
or ignore your sunset despite the bluster
that stings my face, after all, it does
blow apart the custard clouds
for a better view, even while it sharply
shapes my hair into this anvil,
and drives a cold spike through my ears
and into my skull. Here's to persistence
because you waited a long time for me
to arrive, or is it the other way around?
No, I will listen to your organic whisper,
no need to psychoanalyze, or prescribe
drugs to endure the creamsicle end,
the loss of the day, the sun exiting neither
stage left nor right but plunging straight
into the ocean. Who was that I saw
walking your sand, cast in bronze
with manicured toes, and her unsaid
riddle of gaze shot into the heart
of the wind where gulls cry out my jealousy.

Visit to Isla Negra

Home of Pablo Neruda
—1 February 2019

Brian Cronwall

1.

Leaving Santiago's Friday morning traffic,
its red taillights like the eyes of tired cats
creeping backwards in the tunnel.
The Mapocho River's brown water rushes
over itself below cardboard huts and piles
of garbage and erratic graffiti of the angry,
naïve, and unsigned. Just beyond the brown haze
of midsummer's dry and slumbering Andes,
telephone wires bring communication over
and in the wind, rocks, and soil. The buildings
fade away like a dream yielding
to flat land, vineyards, the valleys
of the coastal range, squares of green
like quilt patchworks. Soon, eucalyptus
and firs, saline smells and dropping temperatures,
and, then, the Pacific, blue and breaking
on hard granite behind the poet's home and smile.

2.

I arrive at Isla Negra as a pilgrim, his stanzas
and waves carried in me as words, images, rhythms.
Maybe it's in the colored clear glasses of red,
green, blue, orange, which Neruda declared
"makes every drink taste better," or the butterfly
collection's long-tails, whites, monarchs, purples,
or the shells of all shapes, spirals and flats. Maybe
it is the prow figureheads, the gyroscope, the carvings
from Rapa Nui, the guitar and atlas and maps,
the tuxedo he wore to accept the Nobel Prize for Literature,
the bed where he and Matilde slept, made love, awoke
to watch the vast sea ("I am a sailor on land"),
the agate sand below where, maybe, they saw
the silence and grief, the solitude and collective memory,
the damp hope and quiet endurance.

3.

I wonder what it is like
to be inside a wave,
not as a surfer or swimmer
but as a molecule of water,
fragment of kelp,
a small fish spinning
in the cold breakers
or blue sky inside
the waves of the lost
and disordered others?

From the campanile
to the Pacific horizon,
invisible lines
of crash and intimacy,
the views from windows
and comfortable chairs,
the desks where he wrote,
the library of pages
like the leaves of plants,
succulents outside,
the sea and sun's inspiration.
I wonder what it is like
to be inside a wave?

4.

Twelve days after the coup that cut down the crops
he and Allende had planted in the soil of Chileans,
Pablo died of cancer and a broken heart. It took
nearly nineteen years before summer brought
his and Matilde's bones back to Isla Negra,
buried where he wanted, overlooking the vast
"big and messy and blue...in front of my window."

I breathe in all I can see and hear and taste and smell.
Isla Negra, neither an island nor black but now
truly Pablo's island, hard sanctuary, dark knowledge
that took in details of everything, transmuting them
into poetry. And that is what I have found,
like a dispersed holy grail, a fern sending spores

everywhere, an admiration of table legs and sundials,
telescopes and maps, the sacredness of objects
and the nearness of human beings going about their lives
drinking pisco sours and eating conger broth,
laughing and letting their tears water the fertile hearts
of men and women whose hands I can hold, whose lips
I can kiss, whose hunger I can try to slake.

I came as a pilgrim but leave as an acolyte.
May these verses be the singing of new prayers,
homage to Neruda's all-ness, now my friend,
accompanying me on the road back to Santiago.

Try This

Elizabeth Stoessl

and just this once walk
these woods entire
without calculating
how you'd write the moss
the rotting bark   the French doors
so far back in the trees
always that grey face watching
behind the glass   the slipperiness
of the path

and don't try to coerce
a metaphor from those roots
that radiate so far from their
beginnings   they'll trip you
as you plot your potential
rendering of them even
while you are not
seeing them.

Just shut up just
look   just follow
the dog that knows everything.

October Omnium-Gatherum

Jennifer Lothrigel

Subtly striped, pink and glittering,
only if you look close;
heads of Amaryllis Belladonna lay decapitated in my front yard.
Light continues her short-lived romance
with their sticky poisonous petals
even into deep magenta death.

My husband brings home red roses and mini-pumpkins.
The calendula begins to self-sow.
I can feel the extent of my over-extension in my knees.
The hours offer their soft shoulder, the veil is thinning.
I crave early darkness.

I cover my altar with a Hungarian tapestry
my grandmother never finished,
its un-hemmed edges don't reach all the way across.

I've been thinking a lot about what is *really* mine.
Not the flowers, not the witholding of matriarchal love
slowly dripping down
through the lineage,
now nearly dry.

I lend the neighbor eggs.

She brings me chocolate cupcakes with orange frosting.

Her son was the one who chopped down my flowers.

Through the stillness,

little bits of forgiveness creep.

Shy Creature

Michael Milburn

—for my student

Smiles unreturned,
hellos brushed past—
from our first class
she made clear that

charm would not
be any part of her
opening up to me,
for which I didn't

scold her, showing
her that the person
she was capable of
being was the one

I looked forward to,
with mute moments
and unreadable face.
As for whether

my acceptance of her
was the only identity
she attached to me,
I would say yes,

on the model of pets
who approach warily
and let you touch them,
then sleep at your feet,

their affinity for you
as opposed to another
being that you don't
make them cower.

It's Been 50 Years: An A to Z

Sharon Goldberg

Admiral King High School

My high school no longer stands. Its doors opened in Lorain, Ohio in 1961, when Baby Boomers flooded classrooms. In 2013, five years before my fifty year class reunion, the structure was demolished, cheaper to replace than remodel. During my school days, a bronze bust of Admiral Ernest J. King, a Lorain native who commanded naval forces in World War II, rested on a pedestal in the lobby as if he were watching students rush to classes, snooze in study hall, and rock out at dances. In that building, I played Martha Brewster in *Arsenic and Old Lace;* I served as Secretary of The Booster Club and President of Thespians; I cheered at pep rallies and basketball games; I showed up for Y-Teen, Math Club, *Trident* Yearbook, and *Admiral's Log* newspaper meetings; I attended band, choir, speech team, and debate team rehearsals. High school was the center of my life.

Besties

A critical mass of my high school friends, including a group of seven women with whom I gather every year for vacation, attended the reunion. Because we've stayed in touch. Because we were the active and enthusiastic ones. Because we have shared experiences. We even gathered separately at the homes of locals for a Thursday night reunion kickoff and Sunday brunch the day after, quality time to bond and rebond. We laughed again about eighth grade English class when Miss Townsend locked four rowdy boys in a closet. We remembered when Mr. Shook, our Junior High principal, announced over the PA system that President Kennedy had been shot. We talked about knee and hip replacements, about living with Parkinson's and recovering from pancreatic cancer, about conflicts with children and the joy of grandchildren, about travel to England and Australia and Pelee Island, about downsizing and remodeling, about retirement.

Clothes

I obsessed and obsessed and obsessed about what I'd wear to the reunion as if I were a star walking down a red carpet. I ordered 18 items from five stores, six in two sizes: black voile dress, blue bandage dress, floral embroidered dress, print wrap dress, tulle midi dress, off-the-shoulder dress, striped jumpsuit, black and white jumpsuit, and fuchsia ruffled top. I wore the fuchsia top with a black flared skirt. My hair, basic brown in high school and now a shade of red, was freshly cut and colored; my nails manicured and painted purple. At age 68, when I shouldn't give a damn, I still care what people think of me. I wanted my classmates to say, Wow! She looks great. She hasn't gone downhill, deteriorated, degenerated, gotten fat, saggy, old, old, old.

Death

Sixty-one (known) of the 535 of us who graduated are dead. Including Teddy Vukelich, voted funniest in the senior poll, of prostate cancer; Kathy Ross of Crohn's Disease; Ann Edmonds of ALS; Tom McKillip, an electrician, electrocuted; Juanita Brown, one of our graduation speakers, of I don't know what; a former football player, an alcoholic, of liver disease; my green-eyed freshman biology lab partner on whom I had a crush, a rumored suicide. At 18, when you're handed your diploma, you don't wonder which of your classmates will be dead 50 years later.

Ethnicity

Lorain celebrates an international festival each summer, a tribute to the city's ethnic roots and diversity. I flip through pages of the *Trident*. We are Black, White, Hispanic. Our parents or grandparents emigrated from Italy, Poland, Germany, Mexico, Puerto Rico, Russia, Ukraine, Czechoslovakia, Croatia, Macedonia. Our last names are Arredondo, Boycik, Chemerov, Chavez, Hallahan, Pohuliaj, Goldberg, Gigliotti, DeGenaro, Rivera, Stanchak, Heitzenreiter, Kosonovich, Maravich, Elkovich, Cibrowski, Jaworski, Paslawski, as well as Smith, Clark, Cook, Fox, and Miller. Definitely not homogenous.

Flattery

Luis O., who I didn't know in high school, with whom I chatted on the way into German's Villa, asked me to dance—a slow one. "Do you have kids," he asked. "No," I said. "That's too bad," he said. "You're a beautiful woman." Bob V., who I've known since second grade, said, "You look younger than everyone else. You only look 50." "I've had lots of help," I said, but didn't specify my facelifts. Bill S., with whom I "made out" when he was supposed to be helping me with Physics, said I was still a cutie, although I don't remember anyone calling me a cutie when I was eighteen. I'm certain no one called me "beautiful." I devoured the compliments like chocolate truffles. Sincere or not.

Grow Up!

Brenda boycotted the reunion because Sheila, the self-appointed committee chair, a control freak, accused her of stealing or dumping the Memorial photo display from the 45th reunion. Brenda's friend, Carol, didn't attend because Brenda didn't attend. Tony didn't come because he disliked the venue. Mark wasn't there because he RSVP'd after Sheila's deadline. "Rules are rules," she said. High school all over again. (Names changed, of course.)

High School Sweethearts

I had no high school sweetheart. I dated only one boy once from Admiral King. I barely dated in high school at all. I did not marry a person from Lorain or from Ohio like many of my classmates and attend the reunion with him or her. My dates were my gal pals; my life partner Arnie stayed in Seattle. He's from New York City. He has no history with my high school or hometown. We've been together for just 13 years, not decades, so his history with my friends is limited. Without Arnie there, I was free to circulate, linger, reminisce, no worry whether he was having a good time.

Infamous

None of my classmates is famous, but two are infamous. Eleven years after graduation, a woman I'll call Mary Ann, who was estranged from her husband, who was undergoing treatment for emotional problems, suffered an acute schizoid episode. She stabbed her mother and two children to death. The articles on the front page of *The Lorain Journal* about the tragedy featured her smiling senior picture. Mary Ann was found not guilty by reason of insanity. She spent time—I don't know how long—in a mental health facility. She rebuilt her life.

She married again. She attended our 30th year reunion. In 1995, a man I'll call Vincent was found guilty of kidnapping, rape, and felonious assault after holding his former girlfriend hostage in his home. He is still in prison.

When I was in high school I had fantasies of fame. I hoped to be a stage or movie star like Shirley MacLaine or Ann Bancroft. But I will die without an Oscar. Or Nobel. Or Pulitzer. No one has ever asked for my autograph. Most likely, no one will. Fortunately, I've lost interest in fame—too invasive. But I still care about recognition.

Juxtaposition

While we were in town for the reunion, my friend Cynthia and I stayed with our dear friend Dia. Dia spent countless hours assembling a video from pictures that classmates sent to her along with photos from our yearbook, a keepsake for each of us in a blue or gold bag—the school colors. The day after I arrived in Ohio, Dia's cousin Craig phoned her. His sister June, one of Dia's closest friends, had suddenly become critically ill and was dying from sepsis. The following day, Dia learned that her nephew Jeffrey, who had cancer, was in hospice. In the midst of celebrations, girls' lunches, and laughter, Dia consoled June's daughter, arranged family travel to Chicago for June's funeral, and fielded phone calls, emails, and texts about Jeffrey's condition.

Life goes on. Life ends.

Kids

"What was I like in high school?" I asked my friend Bonnie. "How have I changed?" Her viewpoint is more objective than my own; she's a clinical psychologist and has known me since we were kids. Bonnie described me as sheltered back then and basically a rule follower, conflicted about some of my parents' values but not openly rebellious. "But you demonstrated courage," she said, "by auditioning, performing, going for it." Later, she watched me grow into someone who declared independence and was eager for experiences. Now she sees anxiety and obsessiveness. (I know those well.) But, she said, with it comes thoroughness, preparation, relentlessness, commitment to what I want to achieve. And that's what she saw all along.

Lorain

When I was growing up, Lorain was a thriving, blue-collar, rust-belt city of more than 78,000 people, home to U.S. Steel, Ford, United Shipbuilding, Thew Shovel. Now, like other factory cities in Ohio, Indiana, and Pennsylvania, Lorain struggles. The population has diminished to 64,000. Well-paying jobs are scarce. In 1968, Admiral King was one of three high schools in the city. Now Lorain has only one. No one from my family still lives in Lorain. If it weren't for class reunions, I would not go back.

Menu

We dined on meat in gummy gravy billed as carved roast beef au jus; overcooked green beans with mushrooms; frozen vegetable medley; rubbery lasagna; acceptable parsley potatoes; ham that I didn't try; decent appetizers and desserts. But a reunion is about the people, not the food.

Nineteen Sixty Eight

The year we graduated, Lyndon Johnson was President, "Hey Jude" was the Number One song, *2001: A Space Odyssey* and *Funny Girl* were the top grossing films, and the death toll in Vietnam reached

16,592. At 12:10 a.m. June 5, graduation day, Robert F. Kennedy was assassinated. I find it shocking now that his murder did not dampen our joy and celebration.

Out-of-Towners

One hundred sixty-one classmates and their partners attended the reunion, 56 of whom live in 16 states other than Ohio. I've lived in Washington, DC, Los Angeles, and San Francisco in addition to Seattle. Even during Lorain's prime, I yearned to leave. I craved more culture. More opportunities. A big city life. I was drawn to the East Coast, then the West. But my friends who still live in the area are content.

Pogies Clubhouse

On Friday night, we gathered for a mixer at Pogie's Clubhouse owned by Bob Pogorelc, one of our classmates. We ate lemon pepper chicken and pulled pork, baked beans and coleslaw, watermelon and homemade desserts. We brought our own booze. Strukely & Cole (Terry Strukely is a classmate) played music from the sixties and seventies—The Beatles, The Animals, The Rolling Stones, Simon & Garfunkel, Seals & Croft, Neil Diamond, Three Dog Night, The Zombies. Our music. The best music. As comfortable as old penny loafers. Am I locked in a groove like a broken record?

Questions #1

I posed two questions to many of my classmates—an ice breaker, a gateway to revelation. The first: What are you most proud of? Here's what they said:

My kids. My two kids. My daughters and their values. I raised three sons and what cool people they are. My children and that they're in helping professions. Getting my older son through life. The work I did with my daughter getting her through college. How much I've learned through experience. I take care of myself and give a ton to others. The work I did in New Zealand (with MCI, the telecommunications company) that transformed the country. My joyful perspective on life that sustains me. I was dating a woman whose ex broke into the house with a gun. I talked him down and was able to grab the gun. I called the police and got out alive.

My response: I'm proud of what I've accomplished as a writer, especially with a late start. I'm proud of my relationship with Arnie. I'm proud that I've done some good in the world and, hopefully, little harm.

RSVPs

Why did we attend the reunion? Because we have fond memories, because we're curious, because our friends were going, because we've never gone to a reunion, because we've always gone to reunions, because we had fun at the last reunion, because we live in town, because we don't live in town, because we hope to reconnect, because fifty is a milestone, a big deal, because we're alive. If you hated high school, if you want a complete break from the past, if your life sucks, you don't attend reunions.

Senior pictures

Our name tags were copies of our yearbook photos, the names impossible to read because we all need reading glasses. But I was universally recognized anyway despite my nose job and red hair. Apparently, I still look like me. In 1968 we exchanged wallet-sized versions of those pictures and inked messages on the back: "RMA—Remember me always." "To a very sweet and cute girl with a great sense of humor," "You're witty and charming even if you lack the coordination to catch half-dead frogs in biology," "Never forget all the fun in choir & the operetta." "Don't forget the wild classes we had with Judy, Keith, and Briola." "I will forever remember the spark you added to my high school experience." "Our conversations, serious and otherwise, will be remembered along with Sharon and her dreams of the theater." "Give my regards to Broadway if you get there before me." "I'll never forget your craving for hot fudge sundaes."

Teacher

Eleven of our teachers joined us at the reunion, including Mr. Bakalar who taught Speech 1 and 2, who coached the speech team and debate team, who advised the Booster Club, who championed school spirit. We chatted and I told him he was the teacher who had the greatest impact on me. He said I'd told him the same thing at the reunion five years before. He's eleven years older than me, nearly 80, and his memory is better than mine.

Unexpected

One of my elementary school best friends, who I'll call Nancy, approached me early in the evening and said we should talk later. Oh, no, I thought. I knew why. My first published essay "Grandma's Grocery Store" included an account of my experience with one of the store's stock boys, Nancy's brother, who was a teenager. I didn't use his name, but his identity was still obvious. "Junior" would perform tricks with me—lift and twirl me in the air, turn me upside down, balance my feet on his knees—if I played "Operation" with him, a game that involved pulling my underpants below my belly button (but not all the way down). I never expected Nancy to read my essay; it appeared in a print journal. But the memoir is also on my website. Nancy must have Googled me and read it. She apologized for her brother's behavior. I felt terrible. I thanked her but said she owed me no apology. I was not traumatized by the experience. She was not responsible for his actions.

Other surprises: Barb H. who attended a class reunion for the first time told me I was always nice and energetic with lots of ideas. How kind of her to say so. Jack M. who I've known since nursery school, who didn't recognize me at the last reunion, was very friendly and seemed anxious to chat. My longest conversation was with John T., a Lutheran minister, who offered a prayer to start the evening's program. We talked about an intelligence in the universe, what I'd call the "God Concept," one in which John believes passionately and one which I doubt. Hardly a conversation I expected to have at a reunion.

Veterans

As part of the program, the Daughters of the American Revolution (DAR) honored the 23 veterans present from our class, the men and one woman who served in the military during the Vietnam War. The war of my generation. The war I protested. The war that hung over us like smog.

What do you still need/want to learn?

The second question I asked my classmates. Here's how they answered:

Learn more about how music works. How to play a better golf game. An easy way to hit a high note on a clarinet. Learn another language. Learn about other cultures. How to be a more understanding and sympathetic person. It doesn't matter what I learn as long as I'm learning and growing. How to get rid of Trump. How to pray without ceasing all the time. Why we're here. How to explain to the secular world about the presence of a being that gives us a reason for being here. How to age gracefully and die with dignity.

My answer: To be mindful, less reactive, more compassionate toward others and myself. To stop fearing death.

Xenodochial (being friendly to strangers)

I said "hi" to people I didn't know in high school and chatted with most anyone, as if I were a public relations representative. I wanted all my classmates to feel welcome and have a good time and attend the next reunion. I was nice to everyone except the abusive ex-husband of one of my closest friends who doesn't know I know what an asshole he is. I blew him off. Then I felt badly, so I spoke to him later.

Yardstick

For me, a reunion is a check point, a measuring tool, an opportunity to evaluate myself in the context of my peer group and in the context of time. How am I holding up? Are my bones creakier? Are their minds sharper? Are they more at peace? Are they still trying to figure out life as I am?

Zan, Zilena, Zilch, Zilka, Zubal, Zudell, Zych, Zwolinski

Eight of my classmates have last names beginning with Z. Of those, Gary Zych, Keith Zudell, and Laurie Zilch attended the reunion. Gary contributed a black and white film of the dress rehearsal of *Arsenic & Old Lace* to the keepsake video. Five of us from the Class of '68 were in the cast. I watch me as Martha Brewster, one of the crazy old ladies who poisoned even older men to put them out of their presumed misery. Gary played my nephew Mortimer. My friend Ellen Ecker played my sister Abby. Bonnie played Elaine, Mortimer's fiancée. Tom Yannetti played Officer Keene. I still remember my entrance line in the play, spoken with a wobbly old-lady voice, "Well, now, isn't that nice."

Fifty years have passed like a blip on an EKG. The five of us are still here. If we have a 55th or 60th reunion, who knows? But for now, I feel gratitude. I feel blessed. I feel very, very lucky.

You float

Henry Wise

Clear now   in my sight   from *Zhong Shan Lu*
        for Chiang Kai-shek   like one in every town
        like everything on the surface   of this lake   of life
in your leopard print coat   your hair done up   shop lights
like stars   all around   as if you want to be a question
                        no need to ask
                like a mosquito I will tell you   both   I love you
    both
            you
            your mother
                    breadfruit trees puzzle
        the solitary   streetlight   your face   a shadow
        you look like Mazu   your watery hairy   our fingers
long   calloused   pulling me into your gravity
        remember   the age of almost   loving   that generation
we never spoke   the almost imperceptible
        hair   like feathers   on your legs
and I will tell you too   people age   but waves
            never do
        I am remembering you   looking back through   this water of
my dreams   why are streets named
        for that motherfucker   in this part of the island

You float

where we all want independence   but see   I am too
involved   and this island   we share   is split
                                          I know   I now
          must   build up something   say something   leave
something   in this wake
          please remember me   not as I am   embarrassed to be
     but as the young man   who   new to the island
could not speak to you   who then could not even talk
          and clutched you from behind   as you drove your motorcycle
     (unladylike and lovely)   and almost   never
          let go

Charcoal Nude

John Sibley Williams

Roughed-up: edges   indistinct: body
softly black & blending with all this white
                              space. The paper:

less a canvas than a mirror.   That she is displayed here at all
is a minor miracle, the kind the old folks call
                              assimilation.

          Not pictured:

the artist: his intent: that half-moon smile
when the legs are complete   & the infinite
                              opening between.

Weaponized beauty, that we are meant   to touch
ourselves with suspicion. Or is it guilt? A sordid history erased
                              or on full display, depending on

the context. The framed notecard doesn't give us

                              her name.

Ephemeroptera

Corey S. Pressman

Rise and fall,
tiny white flies
mark the moment
this marshy stream
surrenders color
to the sky.

The ephemeroptera
bob and weave in
the cove
safe from swallows
rehearsing curvature
over the sharp grass.

I am here too,
I measure the
lilac bruise bloom
     in slate air,
I accept the confusion
     of cattails.

Squat on the horizon,
the Three Sisters
pretend
not to notice,
    brooding long,
    broad, and blue

beneath Flight 49,
where seventeen souls

stare down silent, astonished
at the flat majesty—

their mute craft pulls a
cumulus cord of

the softest possible pink
right over my head.

Evolution

Riley Danvers

Happiness used to be tingles over skin when you came close;
It was tickle fights and movie marathons and nakedness;
It was date nights of happy hour fondue and Cherry Coke;
It was insatiable desire and searching your body
For secrets you kept locked away.

Happiness now is a single day when I don't have to wonder if you love
     me;
It's whiskey and stand-up comedy specials and clean blankets;
It's swallowing the fight that catches in my throat so you can look at
     me without disdain;
It's murdering pieces of myself to make more room for you;

It's telling myself I could live without you just to relieve the tightness
     in my chest.

Knockin' on Heaven's Door

Jacob D. Thompson

They said he died peacefully in his sleep, but I saw the look in his eyes. They were the eyes of a man in great pain and shock. My grandfather, who I knew as Papa, really had no blood relation to me. But that never stopped his love for my brother and I. He died on a cool April morning, before sunrise. Tristan, Thomas and I were probably still out running amok. My brother was in bed just one door down. The man who was supposed to be watching over us, Dale, a close friend of Papa's, came with a healthy supply of morphine and two cases of beer. I can't say for certain where he was when it happened. My mother, absent like always, was in California with her new boyfriend, whom she met only a week prior. She said to us, "I'll be back on Sunday." She never thought that tragedy could strike us in such a short amount of time. I didn't either.

1
"That long black cloud is comin' down"

Mom was gonna be away, which meant of course, it was time to kick back and have ourselves a small, reasonable party. It was a pot luck of drugs, booze, and junk food. Courtney, the preppy girl who never truly belonged with our pack of stray dogs, provided most of the snacks. She came around the side yard to my back porch carrying a case of Arizona ice tea. I didn't give a fuck about the tea, but I suppose others were thrilled to have something to drink other than alcohol or tap water. Aiden, the greasy busy body who lived down the road, brought a bunch of pills from his neighbor he called "Floaters". Thomas, the long haired and long legged skater, brought his speaker and a soundtrack of rock and roll music. Tristan, our friendly neighborhood pot dealer, brought Persephone, his two foot bong, and an ounce of weed. Kaden and Jared, the red headed cousins brought a couple of beers and some treasured snacks. But mostly they were just along for the ride. We smoked, we snorted, we drank, we laughed, we ate, and we danced to the music, just following the footsteps our parents left behind. We never thought about the consequences of tomorrow because, if we had it our way, there would be no tomorrow. But soon, Bob Dylan's melody would play on repeat, and we would laugh and dance no more.

We all became acquainted with death that weekend. We were so young, and yet we had already gambled our lives and safety too many times to count. Of all the fucked up shit we put into our bodies, it was too much caffeine that almost killed one of us. The look in my friend Tristan's eyes as he clenched his chest in agony is one I'll never forget. While we were all partying Tristan had snorted some floaters and needed to get the damn taste out of his mouth. He drank two Arizona iced teas, and a few minutes later he quietly got up and went inside.

The party never stopped on the back porch, and fifteen minutes had gone by since we had seen Tristan. I wasn't concerned—I just thought he was taking a shit. I started out the night drinking wine from a box I found in my mother's room. Every time I finished my little water bottle full of wine I'd have to retreat back to my mom's room for a refill.

As I walked down the hallway to my mother's room I saw a sliver of light under the bathroom door, so I pounded on it, "You taking a ten ton crap in there or what?" I asked with a smile on my face.

He called out to me from behind the door, "J.T., help."

"I'm not gonna wipe your ass for ya if that's what you're asking for."

Tristan managed to open the door from the bathroom floor. He was shirtless and his long black hair was wet with sweat. His face was white as a ghost. When I saw the seriousness of the situation, I looked behind me to see if any of the kids were lurking around.

"What the hell's going on?" I asked.

"I think I'm having a heart attack, man."

"That's impossible," I said.

"Feel my chest."

I knelt down and put my massive hand on his scrawny chest. Deep in his chest was a malfunctioning heart. I stood up at once and asked him if I should call for an ambulance. He ordered me not to. I told him I'd be right back and I left, closing the door behind me. I went into Papa's room. He was the smartest guy I knew; surely, he'd know what to do.

"Papa, Tristan's having a heart attack in the bathroom," I said shaking in fear.

Papa, lying in bed with an oxygen tube up his nostrils turned towards me. "Well, get him out of here! Call his mother. Have her deal with him."

"He doesn't want to see his mother damn it! Do you have any Advil or Ibuprofen? Isn't that supposed to help?"

"It won't hurt, I've got some in my drawer here. But get that kid out of our house. We don't need this right now."

I grabbed the Advil from the drawer and left the room. Before I headed back to the bathroom I made a stop at my mom's room. I refilled my water bottle full of wine. I chugged the whole bottle and refilled it again, then went back to the bathroom. I gave Tristan some water and the Advil. I closed the door behind me and I did the only thing I could do—I kept him company. Tristan went stiff with pain. I cried beside him, and drank. Soon our friends began to knock on the door.

"What's wrong!" Courtney asked.

"What the hell are you guys doing in there?" Jerrod wondered.

Neither of us answered; we just sat and waited out the pain. I thought he was going to die—one of my people was going to die. Having a heart attack at sixteen years old is almost unheard of, but when Tristan told me that's what he was having, I believed him. When the smoke cleared and the tears dried, we looked to the night stars for answers. All the neighborhood kids had gone home. It was just Tristan, Thomas, and I. Our backs in the soft grass, we came to the conclusion that death was near and he wanted one of us. If not Tristan, then who? The next morning we awoke to policemen in the house. Papa was dead.

2

"Knock, knock, knockin'"

I was fourteen years old the first time I left the west coast. My mom, brother and I went to Rhode Island to visit my Aunt. Aside from the rockin' clam chowder, it wasn't anything special. When we landed back in Oregon, Papa picked us up in his Blue Buick. The car had some nasty smell that reminded me of cat piss. Papa swore it wasn't cat piss, that it was just water damage. The ride back from the airport was a long one. Papa was coughing and had to open the windows for fresh air.

"Are you still sick Papa?" I asked because he was sick when we left and it had been over a week.

"I tried to tell you guys I was sick."

Papa proceeded to tell us that while we were away on vacation, he spent his time in doctor's offices. As I listened to him talk I remembered that he started coughing as far back as our old apartment. We were moving out and he couldn't pack up his records, he was out of breath. He explained to us very carefully that he had been diagnosed with interstitial lung disease. "I'll have to start breathing with an oxygen tube from now on," he said.

"Will you still be able to work?" my mother asked. Of course she was worried about money.

"I don't know Julia," he said.

"Can it be cured? The sickness?"

"No."

3
"Take this badge from me,"

My mother sat my brother and I down on Wednesday and told us her plans for the coming weekend. We were not thrilled with the short notice planning, but that was her way. She had met some new guy named Roland who was only two years younger than Papa, and she wanted to go with him to California for his son's funeral. During that time, Dale would be coming to watch over Papa, who was terribly sick at this point. She told me that Dale would be sleeping in my bed and I would get to sleep in her Queen size Tempur-pedic. I had no problem giving up my plain mattress on the living room floor. I did, however, have a problem with Dale coming to stay with us for an entire weekend. Back in November, we had to have Thanksgiving with the bastard. Only a few weeks before that, mom told us that he had tried to burn down his house with his family still inside. Mom didn't want him in the house back in November, but, by April, she'd decided to let the man stay for an entire weekend, in her son's bed no less. Isaac and I tried to argue with her. We didn't feel safe with the guy. She told us that Papa had requested that Dale stay through the weekend because he didn't trust me with all my friends. Our protests ceased.

When Dale arrived, he kept trying to party with me and my friends. He kept offering us the beer in the fridge, so we entertained the guy for a while. We gave him a rip from Persephone and the guy disappeared for a while. We found him nodding off in the living room, midstance. That motherfucker, was completely unaffected by his own friend's death. After the paramedics hauled the body away, Dale made up Papa's bed and took a nap in it. Maybe it was the morphine that numbed him, but I don't buy it for a second. My Papa was sick as a dog and he asked his crazy-ass pal with enough drugs to kill a horse to "take care of him" for the weekend. I mean, shit, if I hadn't been so fucked up at the time, I would have seen it coming. But I suppose that was part of the plan too. Dale arrived with two cases of beer, but those weren't for him, pill popper that he was. And the beers certainly weren't for the sick man in bed. The alcohol was there to keep me blind to the facts. That motherfucker killed him. And Papa had asked him to.

4
"It's getting dark, too dark to see"

For all we knew, Tristan had had a heart attack the night before. Whatever it was, he'd survived, and we were exhausted. I wanted nothing more than to sleep in late. But I awoke to commotion coming from outside my mother's room. The door to the room was wide open. Outside of it stood a tall man dressed in blue. I jumped out of the bed and got my shoes and hat on, in preparation for a getaway. I thought that the cops might be there for me. After all, I had a tub of weed in the backyard and paraphernalia throughout the house. I quickly came to realize that they had no way to prove that all those things were mine, so I quickly tore off my hat and shoes. Thomas woke up in what he'd worn the night before. He looked disheveled and worried. I'm sure I matched his look. He asked me what the hell was going on. I told him the cops were here. His eyes went wide.

A moment later the cop entered my mother's room. "Jacob?" he asked.

"Yeah, that's me," I answered.

"I'm sure you understand the situation," the blue man assumed.

"What situation? What are you talking about?" I asked.

"Your grandfather passed away last night in his sleep," he said without expression.

"Oh shit," Thomas said as he looked at me.

All noise was gone. The cop kept speaking but I heard nothing. I looked at all the trinkets on my mother's shelf, trying to comprehend the five minutes that had just occurred. The nine words I just heard shattered like glass and I had to pick up the pieces just to understand. A man who had been in my life since day one was gone. The memories flooded my mind like a cup with too much water in it. Papa at the helm of his Alfa Romeo, the top down, the wind in his hair, and me by his side in the passenger seat. We were heading into the desert on our way to an old car rally. It was our job to take pictures of all the classic cars.

"We have to be on Rally behavior Jake," he said with his eyes on the road.

"I know Papa. Can I take pictures too?" I asked in desperation.

"Of course, we're photographers now. Say, who's Papa's boy?"

"I am!"

"That's good to hear!"

As that memory faded another came to replace it. I was having one of my head crushing migraines. I sat on the table in the nurses room at school. The office had been trying to get a hold of my mother for and hour or so to see if she could come pick me up. But it was Papa who entered through the door of the nurse's office.

"Hey Jake, whaddya say we get out of here and get some ice cream, huh?"

He saved the day more times than I can count. He provided for us when my mother wouldn't and my father couldn't. He showed up when no one else did. He was my hero and he died sick and in pain. I began to panic; I didn't get to say goodbye. My last interaction with him wasn't all that pleasant. All I wanted to do was tell him that I was Papa's boy, one last time. I know that would have made him happy. Another memory came to me then, that calmed me.

Months before that tragic day I was crying at my computer. It was late and I was writing a story that too closely resembled my life. I heard dry coughs coming from Papa's room and shortly after I heard his door open. He was getting up to get a glass of water. When he saw I was crying he stopped. He grabbed a chair and sat next to me. He put his arm around me.

"What's goin' on Jake?"

"None of this is ever going to change. Mom all twacked out on drugs, dad's doing the same elsewhere, and you're sick. I can't take it anymore!" My tears were suddenly stunned by anger.

Papa rubbed my back, "It's been an honor being apart of your life. I know you'll do great things."

And he got up, filled his glass with water, and went back to his room. That was his goodbye to me, I didn't know it then, but as I stood by my mother's shelf with a cop looking down on me, I knew. He was gone.

There were more strangers in my house than there was family, the morning of his death. It didn't make any sense. Why did I have to hear such horrible news from a stranger who would be gone in twenty minutes, taking the corpse with him. I would be left to bear the heartache. The cop asked me to come see the body. I nodded and followed him out the door. He was sprawled out on the bed, his mouth hung open, eyes bulging red. I wondered if someone could die in their sleep with their eyes open. In the living room, Dale spun a story. Tristan sat on the couch, his hat and sunglasses were already on. We shared a look that spoke: "Death really was here."

5

"Heaven's Door"

My mother always wondered why I preferred my friends' company over hers. It was because I never had to ask them to be there for me. After all the cops and strangers left, Dale took a nap on my grandfather's death bed, Tristan and Thomas sat in my living room not knowing what to do, my brother retreated to his girlfriend's house, and I just stood there for a while. The red headed cousins came knocking at the door. They both gave me a hug and the five of us made our way to the back porch.

"We really need some music man," Tristan insisted.

Thomas went to turn on his speaker, but it was dead. He looked at us defeated.

"Papa has…had…a speaker. I suppose he won't be using it anymore, huh?" I said with a slight chuckle.

My friends looked at me as if they were waiting for me to break. I went back inside to retrieve Papa's speaker. On the way to his room, I grabbed a pair of sunglasses and put them on. I couldn't bear to look anyone in the eyes. I made it to Papa's old door. Inside was a doper who almost certainly had a hand in this tragedy. I needed him out of my fucking house, so before I grabbed the speaker, I stole his damn morphine. I figured that would be the only way to get to him. He was gone before the day was through.

I threw Tristan the speaker and sat back down. Waiting for some cheerful music and a hit out of Persephone, I couldn't help but think about Papa's red bulging eyes. The look of death. I watched Tristan as he tried to figure out this speaker. He found the on button and pressed it. Immediately, Bob Dylan's "Knockin' on Heaven's Door" began to play. I looked at Tristan.

"That ain't fuckin' funny," I said.

"I'm not playing it," He said sincerely. "It must still be connected to your grandpa's phone."

We all sat there and listened. When the song was over, it started again from the top. I don't know how many times we listened to it. All I know is that I was listening to the last thing my Papa ever heard. I realized then that my suspicions were true. Papa knew his time was up. I looked around at all my friends. They didn't have to be there. They could have high tailed it out of there like my brother or Dale after he saw his morphine was missing. But family is a group of people that stay together. And at the time, they were the only family I had.

As I listen to this song again I am reminded of these friends who stuck by me in the worst of times. I don't see much of them anymore, but I know when I do, it'll be the same as it ever was. Tristan slept for a good two days on my couch before he went back to his mom's. It turned out he had heart palpitation issues and caffeine was something he should quit consuming. My mother didn't come home for a week, and when she did, all she wanted from me was the morphine I had stolen. No hugs. No kisses. I don't see much of her anymore either. Papa had planned his death perfectly; mom was away and there was enough booze in the house to keep me numb. I was bitter about the whole affair for quite some time, but when I think of it from his perspective, it starts to make more sense. If I couldn't breathe correctly or on my own for two years, would I want to die too? And if the answer was yes, would I call upon my friends for help?

Ask Now

"The questions we never thought to ask the dead pile up."

—Alec Wilkinson in *The New Yorker*

Elizabeth Stoessl

Two ways to manage the pile-ups: foundations
for fictions we'll build to be truly ours
when the dead are no longer here to correct us,
or kindling to flame them away unanswered.
How many of us did you really want?
Did you feel guilt when the fire got your brother?

So why did we not ask? Fear of a father's tears,
a mother's prevarications, igniting
a conflagration too hot for young ears?
And when you and your sister delivered
Aunt Nora's secret baby, was she her own midwife,
using her nurse training to pant you through?

Is this the payback they secretly hoped for
when they'd say "One day I'll be gone and then you..."
Why did you save one letter from some man
who called you a cheating bitch? Who gave you

my "heirloom" ring, not ruby but glass?
Where were you when Nazis came for your mother?

Is our wondering the payback they secretly hoped for
when they'd say "Someday I'll be gone and you…"
even though they would miss the reckoning?
And we who soon will be dead: do we not
feel satisfaction hoarding our secrets
that will burn with us, distraught survivors
finally wanting to know, but too late?

Did you ever love him?

Flat

John Grey

This far out in plain country,
maybe you see people, maybe you don't.
The sky's your nearest neighbor.

Hot and dry most times, rain when wanted
and unwanted, sometimes the thunderhead,
huge and black and threatening

like you're living next door to an angry God.
And tornadoes of course. Land this level,
nothing can stop them. Only prayer tries.

When someone dies, you go visit the family.
When they're not living well, you show up
at their door with stew.

Outside the ritual of planting and harvesting,
all you need remember is church on Sunday
and never leave a gate open.

Flat

Flat land, flat singing in the local choir,
flat broke in the down years,
flat out when work needs doing,

flat days sometimes, flat nights always,
and smart types on either coast
itching to take a rise out of you.

From out the river below, these pilings

Simon Perchik

From out the river below, these pillings
just born and already there wingtips
connect with another shore

though there's no feathers yet and underneath
just water, the instinct to stay still
when there's no wind—it's how all bridges

are built for the dead, the back
that is broken, has to be lifted
held up by another place and you follow

by lowering your head to let the river led
know it is remembered, has a home
though not a star is out, no roofs with chimneys.

Manifest Destiny: Utah Gift Shop Postcard, 1876

Adam Tavel

The foppish engineer has posed before—
coattails fanned, contrapposto as a whore.
Sun glints the droopy U his watch chain makes
dangling at his belt. This is his rightful place,
he thinks, beside three Chinese laborers
morose and half-asleep. They don't confer
but stand on their railway handcar, unfazed
their tracks bolt down the desert's throat. The haze
beyond is craggy scrub and shadscale wilt.
The shortest worker winces back. He's built
so far across the western sand he's cured
himself of hope. The stoner clerk demurred
when I said what the hell. I was his last.
I broke his dream inside the counter glass.

Two Trees

Jeffrey Letterly

Those two trees didn't sprout leaves
     this year, witches against the green summer

and orange autumn. Their gnarled hands reach
     out constantly, ready to grasp

rain and spit it out. In the long winter,
     they will look like all of the others,

bare branches covered with snow
     then lingering grey slush at the base.

They'll keep on surviving into warmth,
     twin sisters laughing and crying,

naked and laughing and crying.

First Waterfall

Suzy Harris

They could feel God's words
like bruises on their tender skin.
They could not meet each other's gaze,
did not try to comfort.

Outside, they found no path to guide them.
Each step was a question: this way or that?
After many steps, steps beyond counting,
Adams throat seized with thirst,

Eve's skin blistered from the pounding sun.
So they stopped—and in that moment,
they heard the sound of water racing over pebbles
and followed the water's call, now louder,

booming like God's voice, only kinder,
through a stand of willows,
where a great storm of water
tumbled over boulders,

pooled in a cleft below.
Adam cupped his hands into the stream,

raised them to Eve's lips.
Eve knew then she had been right—

it was better to know. She tasted
the sweet water, poured the rest
over her head, then dipped her hands
to offer Adam a drink.

Tuesday Morning

Hilary Harper

Laura Cunningham makes her way through the maze of the department store, trying to remember which way she came in so she can get the hell out. It is too hot, too full of scents, and she can't escape the piped-in pop music soon enough. She is looking for the passageway that leads to the parking structure, but can't remember which floor it is on.

She had buttoned her wool coat while standing at the register and now feels trapped inside it. She fumbles at the buttons, a task made difficult by the two large shopping bags she holds. At a cosmetic counter she deposits the bags and opens her coat.

A salesgirl with bright red lipstick appears. "Can I help you?"

"No. Thank you." Laura collects her bags and moves on, certain there must be a directory nearby. She heads toward the escalators where, indeed, there is signage with a map of the store. She is studying the map when she is distracted by the sound of whimpering. Looking down she sees a child on the floor behind a fake potted tree.

The way to the parking structure is clearly marked, just one floor above her, and Laura considers ignoring the child. Surely, she will be found, or someone else will come by and alert the authorities. Laura looks around for frantic parents or an employee who might take charge of the situation, but it's a Tuesday morning, the store is nearly deserted.

The child looks to be about four or five. Wearing blue jeans, boots, and a puffy pink jacket, she sits with her knees pulled up to her chest, and her head, full of dark curls, tucked in.

Laura steps forward. "Hello? Are you lost?"

The child scoots back and increases the grip on her knees. "Oh, for heaven's sake," Laura says. She just wants to get out of the mall and go home. She wants to take her shoes off, have lunch, and then relax in a bath before her book club meeting. Instead here she is, crouching down to talk to a strange child. "Don't be afraid," she says as gently as possible.

The girl removes one arm from around her knees and wipes at her eyes.

"It's okay," Laura says.

The girl lifts her head for a quick peek at Laura.

"Can you tell me your name?"

The girl mumbles something.

"I'm sorry dear, I didn't hear you."

"Sophia," she says loudly.

"Sophia. What a beautiful name. Why don't you come with me Sophia? I'll help you get back to wherever you belong."

The girl shakes her head.

Stubborn kid. This is not Laura's problem, but she feels a sense of responsibility. Having engaged with the child she can't just walk away.

"Do you want to come with me and have some ice-cream?"

The girl looks up at Laura and she is gorgeous: full-face, rosy cheeks, big blue eyes. For a moment Laura is mesmerized, and then Sophia uses the back of her hand to wipe her wet upper lip. Laura reaches into her purse for a clean tissue and hands it to the girl. "Here. Use this."

Sophia snatches the tissue, swipes at her nose, and then stuffs the tissue into her jacket pocket.

"Come on now." Laura extends her hand toward the girl, who tentatively takes it.

Pleased with her success in getting the child to comply, Laura stands up with a sense of accomplishment and some measure of pleasure. It has been a long time since Laura held a child's hand, filthy as it may be.

She is leading the girl back toward the cosmetic counter when a large man rushes toward them and shouts, "Sophia!"

The man grabs the child by her free arm. He is wearing a black knit hat and a black zippered jacket. He yanks the girl's arm so hard he pulls her off her feet.

Sophia screeches.

The man does not seem relieved to have found the child, and he does not look at Laura. He just takes the girl by her arm and demands, "Where the have you been?"

It happens so fast; Laura can hardly react. "Hey," is all she manages to say.

"Let's go." The man drags the girl away as she kicks and cries, leaving Laura standing there, stunned.

They don't get far before the girl's resistance makes the man stop. He smacks her bottom and then lifts her up. He clamps her crosswise across his chest, restraining her flailing limbs with his arms.

The man heads toward the center of the mall where there is a fountain and a food court. Laura follows without thinking about it. The man struggles to keep his grasp on the girl, who continues to wail, drawing the attention of shoppers. People turn their heads, some stop, and then move on, unconcerned. It's just a kid.

Laura feels a hot flush of sweat on her chest and the back of her neck. Her heart is racing, and she is confused. She cannot determine if the child is in danger. Has she been taken against her will, or is the man a brutal father? Is she being abused, or just headstrong and difficult?

The man stops at a bench, sits down, puts the girl on her feet and shakes her. Laura steps into the entrance alcove of a shoe store and watches through a window display. Sophia slumps to the floor and sits with her head in her lap, defeated, as the man takes a phone out of his pocket and makes a call.

Feeling conspicuous, Laura crosses to the other side of the mall. She stops near the elevator tower and turns back to look at Sophia, but sees only the man. He jumps up and looks around, just as Laura spots a blur of Sophia's pink jacket running past her. The girl zips around a corner and goes down a corridor that leads to an exit. Laura immediately follows, moving as quickly as possible without calling attention to herself.

She rounds the corner and sees the girl up ahead, running toward the exit doors. The girl's determination to escape convinces Laura that something is terribly wrong. Sophia slips through a door held open by entering shoppers and Laura increases her pace. Laura dashes out the door, worried the girl will run in front of a car, but there she is, scurrying down the sidewalk.

Laura watches as Sophia ducks behind a bush.

After waiting a moment to be sure the man is not in pursuit, Laura slowly approaches the bush and squats down. "Sophia?"

The girl looks at her with wide eyes.

"It's okay. I won't let anyone hurt you." Laura offers the girl her hand. "Come with me," she says, suddenly knowing what's going to happen. "Quickly," she says.

Sophia takes Laura's hand and off they go, around the side of the mall, into the parking structure, and toward the car. Laura pulls a fob from her coat pocket and the doors of the Audi click. She opens a door and tells the girl to get in.

To All the Boys

Lisa Higgs

She loved a boy who was her brother's friend
who waited for her as they crossed between

hayfield and corn, on the way to the tracks,
who let her catch up because of her child legs'

short stride, and a boy who needed love
like a houseplant watered until its catch-rim

overflowed, and a boy who admitted to loving
summer girl and school girl in overlap,

since neither lived in the same town, and the world
wasn't small enough yet for phones and photos

to give up the game. She loved a man known
for obsessions, which was fine while she was one,

and a man prone to nights in, and waking
much too early, when she'd rather sleep. She loved

a man who wanted more children, and tried guilt.
She loved a man so inconsistent with his time,

he left her waiting. She loved a settled man
whose routine of love was expressed by attention

to her breasts, and a man who slept long hours
in front of the TV, a man who had to be asked

many times to do anything he didn't want to do,
and a man who could not manage to grieve

while deeply bereaved. She loved a man better
and worse than all the rest, this boy prone to jokes,

this man silent unless spoken to, who asked
for a date, uncertain she was of a mood to say yes.

52.

Geoff Cannard

The radio remembers late at night
the music it forgot. It revels in
a playlist built of songs that might incite
the callous day to soft invoke again
the spirit mixed with stone, the old concrete
foundations of a voice that wavers thin
across the years in steady slow retreat
from principals on which it would begin.
But night stays silent save the tunes it plays,
one dream repeated in each longing phrase.

Understory

Nathan Bas

Tip of finger
stamps down on

sandy-flage
carpet eaters.

A shell crunches and guts stain
the white window sill;

others
on their backs
flailing.

More crunches.

And he sticks that tip on his tongue
and says, "extra protein,"
and goes back to work

and I mull like a vegan
and notice

there's satisfaction

satisfaction in the trampling
of understory,

where the beauty lies,
where the children play.

Even down into dirt
on summer vacations
the click and flame of a lighter

ignites wings
in their burrows.

Moments like an ice water wakeup,
life-bucket stings.

But the lack of allergy...
is it right?

Before the backyard gully got ripped out
and packed tight with another set of sad
cookie-cutter homes

the BB's went
into squirrels
into fence line;

claws of chalk on wood.

he aimed through a crack
and knuckled the glass
with his scarecrow hands
when not up for reload,

which was often.

Tiring.
Embarrassing.
Accepted because:

He's my father.

Swerving to kill possums
and eats cows like they're nothing more
than the carpet eaters
on the tip of his tongue.

And the strangest thing is:
he's actually pretty funny.

The Applicant

Marty Walsh

When the applicant went online the applicant
Was instructed to fill out the form that was provided,
Print it, date and sign it and bring it to Suite 107, the
Pell Tower, on the first of the month, which the applicant
Did. All week the applicant was shuffled from line to line,
Suite to suite, before the applicant's application was finally
Okayed. He was instructed to report to Waiting Room L-14 on
Monday and every business day thereafter until the
Interviewer had time to see the applicant. And was further
Instructed: No food. No beverages. No reading material. No
Laptop. No mobile devices, ear buds or tunes. And the
Applicant complied. Waiting Room L-14 was white; white walls,
White floor, and one white chair, which the applicant sat
Down in. Eight straight hours of nothing to do but stare
At the opposite wall. Which the applicant did day after day,
Week after week. Until one Sunday night the applicant picked
Someone up at a bar and overslept ever so slightly and was ten
Minutes late arriving at the waiting room. Whereupon the
Receptionist informed the applicant that an interview opportunity
Had been missed. And that tardiness was frowned on if one
Wanted to be considered an earnest applicant. And so the applicant
Sat and stared day after day. And began to imagine that there

Was a framed painting of a capsizing sailing ship on the
Opposite wall. And imagined getting up and crossing
The room and tilting the painting's frame until the ship righted
Itself. But by the time the applicant had sat down again,
The ship was capsizing once again. And this went on day
After day. And when the applicant expressed exasperation
About how long the process was taking, the applicant was
Informed that impatience was frowned on. Strike two.
Then, eight months later, the applicant was notified that
Due to the applicant's failure to see opportunities and seize
Them (strike three), the applicant was currently no longer under
Consideration for a position. What opportunities? the applicant
Cried. That's not fair! Well, that's life, the Receptionist replied.
Try again. Almost no one gets a face-to-face on the first try. Only
The Interviewer decides these matters. And before having the
Applicant escorted from the premises adding: Most spend their
Whole life and never get a foot in the door. If there's a door...

The Professional Thinker

Thomas Cooper

I was sitting on a bench opposite a fountain when an old woman approached and sat down next to me. After sitting in silence for a few minutes she uttered a proposition that I thought would make me rich:

"A penny for your thoughts my dear."

I spent the next ten minutes frantically saying anything that came into my head before finally pausing and asking for my money. The old woman looked at me in surprise and asked what I meant. I responded that she owed me at least a pound for all the thoughts I'd just offered up. She laughed and got up from the bench to walk away and it was then I realised the robbery that had taken place. Thus, in self-defence, I grabbed a nearby rock and smashed it down onto her head over and over again until I was confident she was dead. Intellectual property is a valuable commodity these days and needs to be protected at any cost.

Fog

Chet Skibinski

The fog arrived on a Saturday evening, and no one bothered to notice. It was still there Sunday morning, much heavier, much denser. Cars moved cautiously, as if driving in a unfamiliar foreign place, using their horns like children might—sounding brave at first, then growing more tentative, a little frightened.

The city had no center, no downtown area of old apartment buildings, and crowded streets. It was a new city, leisurely spread out with small shopping centers and business centers, and thousands of homes. If the fog had come to an older city, maybe the people downtown would have come together—if not to find a way out, then at least to smash windows and riot and bum. But there were no crowds of people here, just families in houses, and couples in condominiums, and single renters in new apartments with broad parking lots that were sheltered for residents, unsheltered for visitors.

By late Sunday night, the fog was the main subject of the local news, but it was a story without a picture—TV reporters standing with a wall of gray behind them. On Monday, commuters tried to drive to work; most never got more than a few blocks from their houses. There were noises of an occasional car, then the sound of a crash—a muffled, fender-bender crash—not serious.

By Tuesday, though, there were hardly any sounds of car engines—no more than one or two an hour. People stayed inside, phoning in to their work places to say they were fogbound at home, some of them laughing self-consciously, almost embarrassed because the reason sounded a little dubious.

A day later, the Internet died. People saw a simple message on their screens: "You are no longer connected to the Internet." Appropriately, this was written in gray—battleship gray letters on a light gray background. And that afternoon, the power went out.

Stores and markets were closed. Even though some probably had portable generators to provide power, no employees were willing to find their ways there in the deep fog. In their homes, people lit candles and set flashlights upright, their beams pointing to ceilings, making circles of light on top of dark rooms. They ate canned food, using camping stoves to heat tiny pots of water for instant coffee, and sat in dim living rooms during the day, with the curtains open, but not able to see the rose bushes four feet away from the window in the wall of fog.

On Saturday, when the phones all went dead, no one seemed surprised. When cell phones didn't work either, people left them in drawers, or set them on tiny decorative tables that were never used for anything anyway.

By Monday, after nearly ten days of fog, people began running out of food. They went out alone, or in pairs, intending to walk to the markets, logically realizing that they'd all be closed, but not being able to think of anything better to do. They told themselves that they'd be careful, that they'd watch their feet as the sidewalk ended beneath them, and a road was crossed, and another sidewalk began. They took heavy, aggressive flashlights with them, but when they turned on those powerful beams, there was nothing there, nothing in front of them, except a wall of pewter gray, and their own lights glaring back in their faces. A few walked only half a block before returning to their houses, feeling small and scared. Those who kept walking were never seen again.

Then there were the ones with their GPS gadgets, who left their houses with a bullying kind of confidence. None of these were ever heard from either. The rumor was that the gadgets simply didn't work. Another rumor was that they worked, but in a kind of mocking error, swearing that the owner's location was in a tiny Indonesian village, or by a nightclub in the seedier section of Munich.

Then an elementary teacher named Michelle Kimball decided that a human chain could be formed, with everyone linking hands. Thousands and thousands of people would join in, the chain would lead them out of the fog, to wherever that might be. So she went door-to-door around her entire suburban block, urging people to join her early the next day. "A human chain is powerful enough to break any other chain," she said, though few really understood how chains and fog were related. But nearly two hundred people started out with her.

For a mile, it worked. The human chain called out and sang songs—old, silly children's songs—as they passed houses. Michelle Kimball blew on an old trumpet. The chain absorbed more and more people; it snaked up and back through neighborhood streets, with Michelle's husband using an old pocket compass to keep track of where they were going—east, away from the ocean, away from the fog. But after a mile or two, the chain stopped. No more joined in. A few people decided to keep following Michelle and her compass husband; the others chose to retrace their steps back to their houses. The compass people headed east, but never left the fog. The returning people got lost in the maze of residential streets; they knocked on house doors for directions, but no one would answer. A day after it had begun, the human chain had dissolved into the fog, and Michelle's trumpet was the last noise that many people heard from outside their locked houses.

After two weeks, people became more desperate, angrier. They began going out in groups of five and six and seven, furiously looking for food now, saying enough is enough. They could be heard talking, arguing, somewhere out there, but the fog was thick enough to cushion the sounds. It was hard to tell how far away the voices were coming from, or what they were saying.

By the beginning of the third week, even the batteries began dying. The portable stereos and radios all became quiet. The flashlights went out. A few people still used candles, and they burned small and sweetly smelling, but were gone in a day or two.

Seventeen years later, the fog lifted. No one rushed into the city, though. They waited a few days, and then the first ones—journalists and scientists and police—made the initial probes. They found the remains of bodies in the houses and apartments. Starvation, dehydration, or whatever—after seventeen years, it didn't matter. More people came, including the inevitable looters, but even the most desperate, hardened looters didn't stay long. A few hours in the city were enough. Besides, the fog might come back. Even with the sky a benignly faded blue, and the horizon visibility at ten or twenty or thirty miles—even then, you couldn't be sure. So they all left. What was left of the corpses stayed in the houses. They were supposed to be removed, but there were arguments as to what authority had the right or the obligation to do the removal work; the arguments went on for weeks, and then slowly melted away, as everyone wanted to forget to do anything.

Over the years, roads became better all over the country. Concrete changed to a hard, indestructible plastic, imbedded with sensors that controlled the traffic effortlessly and automatically. But these motorways avoided the fog city. There was no highway sign because no explanation was needed. Everyone knew. The motorway went straight south, along the coast, and then made a gentle turn to the left, sweeping inland broadly away from the ocean, and then, eventually, curving again, back to an ocean view, the fog city well behind it now. It was rumored that no one dared look behind, to the north, in the direction of the fog city, even in their rear-view mirrors. And some even reached up to cock their rear-view mirrors awkwardly sideways, just in case they were tempted.

The Angel of Dresden

Marc Jampole

Behind the benevolence chiseled
into gracile lips and brooding eyes,
the part of me made of polished rock
cannot cry, doesn't feel the pain of others,
doesn't mourn the limp sacks of skin
that used to breath, eat, sing, love,

Twenty-five thousand of them crushed, twisted,
charred, melted, moldering underneath rubble—
pock-marked blocks of concrete, twisted rebar
and jagged glass that used to fit together tightly.

My open arms beckon to the ruins below
offering the appearance of consolation,
my face reflects a bottomless well of sorrow,
but it's a stone mask, frozen into shape
years before, my current sadness on loan
from those looking up at me, who in other times saw
frivolity, piety, joy or triumph bouncing off my surface.

Devil's Night

Joseph Harris

In social studies the principal comes over the PA and gives the same speech he does every October 30th, telling us about the 10pm curfew, the stepped-up patrol and neighborhood watch, to not disgrace our city or our school or ourselves. When he's done, our teacher Mr. Thomas gives us his two cents. He tells us about how Devil's Night started after the '67 riots, how it's Detroit's—our neighboring city above Eight Mile Road—very own infamous holiday, how it used to be the worst on the east side, where, one night in the 80's, a thousand structures went up in flames.

"Fuckin' dumbass probably lives on the east side of Ferndale," my friend Tommy says under his breath, though he does too. So do I. "The fuck does he know about it?"

"What's the point?" I say, pulling the zipper of my jacket. "The only reason the numbers have gone down is cause there's nothing left to burn."

Victor laughs behind us, sorting candy he stole from homeroom earlier. "There's a little bit left. You just gotta scope it out, that's all."

Chris laughs at Victor, rubs the sleep from his eyes. "We should burn down *your* house," he says.

"My house is nice, man," Victor says, adjusting the brim of his fitted Tigers hat. "Bigger than Mr. Thomas', that's for sure."

The class laughs. Mr. Thomas brushes it off, returns to his lecture.

"This dovetails nicely with our discussion. Drugs fill the economic hole left by industrial work. This inevitably leads to substance abuse, particularly alcoholism, which then leads to jail sentences that, as the system is now constructed, prevents the incarcerated from ever again attaining gainful employment."

Victor throws a miniature candy bar at him when he turns to write something on the board. He turns back and yells at us, louder, but by then we're all laughing. He shakes his head and passes out our homework and sits down at his desk.

Chris crumples his up, pops one of Victor's stolen Milky Ways in his mouth. "Come on, man. He's doing his best."

"Why the fuck do they have a twenty-three-year-old teaching seniors?" Victor says.

Tommy rattles drumsticks on his thigh. "I don't think he had a choice. Would you want to teach us?"

I feel bad for him, too, but don't say anything. As the class talks Halloween plans for tomorrow, who's doing what where, I look down at the prompt: *"What are the differences in opportunity between your parents at your age and you?"*

Tommy and I stop by Victor's locker after class to buy a quarter ounce of weed before Victor's lunch rush. Chris puts his backpack in his locker and grabs his Little Caesars hat and apron.

"You're a clown," Victor says to Chris.

"At least I have a real job," Chris says, throwing his essay on the floor of his locker.

"Right," Victor says. "A 'real' job that pays you eight an hour."

But that's about as much as my mom makes. Tommy's mom and my mom work the late shift at the same dollar store in the mini-mall where Sears and Farmer Jack used to be. They've had to work since that fabricating shop on Hilton closed and our dads packed up and split.

Tommy sees his girlfriend, and they walk away together, both muttering, looking at the ground. I stand off to the side as some Pleasant Ridge kids walk up to Victor.

"You're a lifesaver, man," they tell him. "College campus visits all weekend. Spending forty-eight hours with my parents, fuck, will that stress me out."

"I bet it will," Victor says, winking at Chris and me.

Tommy walks back to the lockers, stands next to me, checks his phone. "Your dad call you yet?"

I shake my head. Since he left, he calls me every Devil's Night once he's had enough to drink. He think it's funny, for whatever reason—I can never understand him that well. Never could.

"At least he still calls you," Chris says behind us. "Haven't heard from mine since last Christmas."

"He still sends you money every month, right?" Tommy asks Chris.

Chris laughs. "Why do you think I'm working?"

"Are they hiring?" I ask Chris. Money's been tight at home—my mom's been on my ass about getting an after-school job if I'm not playing sports.

Victor walks back his locker, then coughs, smiles at me. "You short, Pete?"

"Maybe."

"You guys got my number, right?" he asks Tommy and me.

We nod.

"I might have a job for you. You wanna make a few bucks, have some fun tonight, gimme a call."

After school, Tommy and I sit in my living room playing video games. Every few minutes, I put down my controller and scribble notes down on Mr. Thomas' prompt:

I can't be my father; even if I really knew him, even if I wanted to be…I don't drink, neither do my friends, my dad…our dads… started drinking after they lost their jobs…

Tommy plugs his phone into my speakers and plays new tracks from his SoundCloud—a new project he calls Post-Industrial, electronica spliced with live drums and punctuated with silences recorded in the concrete husks that shadow our neighborhood.

He lights a joint filled with Victor's weed. "Pretty good, right?"

"Put that out, man," I tell him. "You can't smoke in the house."

"Your mom smokes."

"I don't care. Put it out."

"Relax, Pete. Jesus." He throws it out the window. "Really though—what do you think of the new stuff?"

I pause the game and listen to the staccato hi-hats ripple through the somber flap of crow wings. "Not bad." I nod my head to the beat and look out the window at the little kids coming home from the elementary school across the street, pulling keys out from under rocks and letting themselves in the side doors of their small houses covered with fake cobwebs and cardboard tombstones. I wonder where my dad is, what kind of buddy-buddy nonsense he's gonna mumble through the phone tonight. I turn the game back on.

"You going over to Stephanie's?" I ask him.

"Not tonight." He exhales.

"Have you guys told your parents?"

"Haven't decided what to do yet."

"Huh."

"I wish I studied more. Can't raise a kid with a diploma job."

"It's too late for us, anyway."

"What, grade-wise?"

"Well, our dads raised us on diploma jobs."

"Fuck them," Tommy says, eyes on the floor.

Through their living room windows, I watch the kids trying on their costumes for tomorrow night—cheap video game character out-fits from the dollar store my mom works at.

Tommy looks up at me. "What do you think about tonight?"

"What *about* tonight?"

"That 'job' Victor was talking about. You think we should check it out?"

"I don't know."

"What—you scared or something?"

"Fuck you."

"What else are we gonna do? Walk up and see our moms? Buy some chalky Halloween candy? Get a fuckin' costume?"

"Write this essay, man."

Tommy laughs. "You're joking, right?"

"What did you just say to me?"

"What did *you*?"

I don't say anything.

"We could both use the money, Pete."

We both stare at the TV for a while, the bass pulsing through the floorboards, then Tommy calls Victor.

He drives over at midnight.

"Nice house," he says.

"Thanks," I say. I don't tell him it's a rental.

"Parents home?"

"My mom doesn't get home 'till late."

"What about your dad?"

We all laugh—even though we don't know *where* they are, we know where they are.

Victor shrugs. He looks over at a picture of my mom and me from when we went down to Cedar Pointe last summer.

"That your mom?"

I nod.

He laughs. "She's young."

"She's hot," Tommy says, and I punch him in the shoulder.

"Your mom's the same age, dickhead," I tell him. That's true—they were pregnant with Tommy and me at the same time after high school.

"So," Victor says, pulling the strings of his Carhartt, "you guys down for an adventure tonight?"

"If it pays," Tommy says.

"It'll be worth your time. I promise." Victor turns to me. "Where's your liquor cabinet?"

I lead Victor to the kitchen and open the alcove above the sink. He reaches all the way back and grabs two leftover bottles of Everclear from my mom's Labor Day party. I've never touched any of it—my dad got out of control with it before he left, and I don't want to risk developing the same habit. Victor hands me a white t-shirt that's lying on a stool.

"Rip it in half," he says. I do.

He takes the two pieces and gives one to each of us.

"When I tell you when, soak the shirt with the liquor then stuff it back in. When you're ready to throw it, light the part that's sticking out."

"What do we need these for?" I ask.

Victor smiles. "Think of it as…as a useful tool for tonight."

We tuck the bottles under our jackets.

"We're gonna have a blast," he says.

On the way out I pull Tommy back and let Victor walk ahead.

"Are you sure about this?" I say.

He pushes me away. "Come on. It'll be fun."

We drive down my street and then up Nine Mile and stop at a red light.

"Last chance to get out," Victor says, lighting a joint and passing it around.

We don't say anything. I feel around for the ripped t-shirt, pull out my essay instead.

My parents had me after they graduated from Ferndale—my dad had a job lined up at Dynamic Fabricating, a mortgage…When you mentioned alcohol and jail earlier, the first thing I thought of was my dad, of all his DUI's, the assault charges from his bar fights. He can't drive anymore, so can't work anymore, but before his shop closed…before that place closed…Anyways, I feel like a nuisance to my mom, that I just remind her of him, about what she lost…he lost…

I try to concentrate but the weed's gone to my head, the memories bleeding into each other. Victor stares at me through the rear view mirror. "Some dude—one of my clients, he lives in Birmingham—paid me a thousand bucks to burn down that old shop on Nine Mile and Hilton tonight. Says if there's enough fire damage he can buy the property from the bank for nothing."

"What's he gonna do with it?" Tommy asks.

"Fuck if I know. Probably luxury condos or some bullshit like that. None of my business."

I've started to notice them around the east side of the city. It's been five years since the recession hit and Dynamic closed up, and I've seen rusted factories converted into spacious lofts. I've been wondering who has a half million dollars to drop on those things, or why they would want to live there in the first place.

I take a long hit, and as I exhale, I realize where we're going.

"Dynamic Fabricating?" I say.

I see Victor nod in the rear view mirror.

"Revenge," Tommy says, taking the joint from my fingers.

We wind through the side streets and stop by Little Caesars to pick up Chris. He gets in the car next to me and takes off his vest. He has dark circles under his eyes and reeks of pizza dough.

"You ready?" Victor asks, smiling.

Chris shakes his head and says, "Sure," and we shoot through the parking lot, down Hilton, toward the shop.

We light another joint as we inch closer and closer, the street-lights glowing on the windshield. Tommy plugs his phone into the tape deck converter and mouths the bass lines, the noise filling my head, my mouth drying up. Chris' leg starts twitching. He looks over at me. "I asked my boss if there were any openings. 'Told me you can stop in any time and fill out an application."

Victor passes Chris the joint. "He doesn't need that bullshit job."

"Shut up," Chris says. "I don't know if this is a good idea. Won't the cops be patrolling?"

"They axed the night shift last year to save money. I told you that already."

Chris sucks in his chest and looks at Victor. "You're not gonna do it."

"Shut up, man. I already took the money. Can't back out now."

"Then don't do it."

"I told you to shut up, Chris."

"Let me out of the car, Victor."

Victor doesn't answer. He looks ahead at hollowed shell of Dynamic in the distance and turns up the music.

"Let me out!" Chris yells.

It takes me a while to turn my head but when I do I look over to the passenger seat, at Tommy. His eyes are wide open, eyebrows twitching.

"I'm getting out of the car," Chris says.

"No, you're not," Victor snaps back.

"Yes, I am."

Victor locks the doors and turns the music up again, lights another joint. The bass shakes the teeth in the back of my jaw.

Victor stops the car at a red light. Chris unlocks the door and gets out.

"Get the fuck back in the car, man! Easiest money you'll ever make!"

Chris slams the door and takes off down a street.

Victor leans over and yells out the window. "All right then, bitch! All right! Walk the fuck home, coward!"

The light turns green and we speed forward, and I watch Chris disappear in the rear view mirror.

We snake through the alleys and park in the back of the loading dock. Abandoned cars litter the parking lot, windows gone, stuffed with tin cans, ragged sleeping bags. It's dark outside except for the quartered moon. Victor turns the headlights off. He gets out quietly, then pops the trunk and pulls out two 5-gallon gas cans. Tommy and I get out with our bottles.

I look around the lot, then past rusty fences to the jack-o'-lanterns shimmering on the porches of the surrounding bungalows. We're all alone. I tuck the bottle under my jacket and walk up to the bay doors.

They used to be painted some neutral color, at least that's what I think as I look at them. All the windows are broken. It already looks burnt.

Victor pulls a hammer from his jacket. He breaks off the padlock and lifts up the door.

There are a few pieces of old ripped-up furniture on the main floor. Moonlight breaks through the jagged glass of the windows and spills onto the dusty concrete, flecks of epoxy spitting light at us. I stare through the weed's hazy filter at beer cans, liquor bottles, cigarette butts, discarded ends of joints, blunts. The walls are torn open where the copper wire's been pulled out.

Victor starts pouring gas on the floor, on piles of squatter's garbage, broken pallets used for firewood. Tommy and I watch him as he works. I remember, briefly, coming here with my dad years ago, a company party or Bring Your Child to Work Day, standing on the spot where my dad showed me how he ground off bubbled material from bad welds that Victor now pours gas on.

When Victor's done we walk together up the creaking staircase to the manager's offices.

"Chris' dad used to work up here," Victor says. "I think that's where he gets his attitude about work from. Management will do that to you."

Victor splashes gas on everything and then leaves the room with Tommy. I stay and sit down on the floor and try to breathe; my heart is beating out of my chest and my mouth is arid from Victor's joints. I reach into my jacket to feel the pumping blood and find my essay in the breast pocket. In the corner of the office, I see an old dresser, oak or some other fine wood with clean edges, brass knobs, its dusty mirror intact. It's the same my mom has in her bedroom. I uncap a pen.

My grandma took this beautiful dresser with her when she left the city after the '67 riots and gave it to my mom as a wedding present; she still does her hair in front of it before she goes to work in the afternoon or the bar on her day off on Saturday night...

I brush the dust from the mirror, stare at my refection.

I wonder how she looked...at herself...to herself...if opportunity, or the lack of it, leaves marks on your face...scars that set your dreams in time...

I look at the walls of the room, covered with graffiti. I try to decipher the scripted letters, the handiwork of one of the crews from school until I hear Victor yelling downstairs, telling me he's done and we need to get out. I pull out my bottle of Everclear and leave the room. And as the gas leaks into my socks, I think that the three of us *should* be here—eighteen, sick of school, bored and frustrated and ready to work, like our fathers eighteen years ago; we *should* be here, high, in one way or another, moving from station to station, fashioning raw metals into something they're not.

"Hey." It's Tommy's hand on my shoulder. "You okay?"

But we *are* here—working, we are here.

"I'm fine." I try to listen for the noises of my dad, but I only hear Victor, mouthing the bass lines of Tommy's new songs, the cadence perfectly matching my conclusion to Mr. Thomas' essay:

I can never be my father, even if I wanted to.

We walk outside to the curb then turn to face the building. We reek of fuel. I look around and check for other people, listen for sirens before I remember what Victor said about the night shift and realize our principal lied to us about the extra cops. It's silent.

Victor looks at me. "Let's light it up."

I nod my head.

Victor looks at Tommy, who's shaking.

"Come on, man. Do it," Victor says.

Tommy tries to twist the cap off his bottle but his hands are shaking too much.

I stand there with my own bottle, struggling with its weight. I twist the top off, reaching into my pocket for the half rag Victor gave me. I pause, then put the rag back and stuff in my essay instead.

"Do it!"

Tommy stands next to me and tugs at my bottle. I think I hear him say something, but all I can think about is my dad.

I grab the lighter from Victor, light the paper and throw the bottle.

The floor catches, burning a bright blue. It reaches the piles of trash, but they're too wet to catch. The pallet splinters smolder, but they've already exhausted their use.

Within a few minutes, the gas has burnt out, evaporated. Just the smell remains—hot garbage, rotten wood.

I look over at Tommy. He's still shaking.

Victor stands silently. I look at his face, covered in gas and sweat and I can't tell if he's crying. "You were right," he says.

"What are you talking about?" I ask.

"In class earlier. There's nothing left to burn."

We linger in the bay opening for a while, not speaking, listening to the cars on the freeway. Then we pull the doors down, get back in the car, and drive away.

The car ride home is silent. Victor keeps the stereo off, hands us our share of the money. "Don't tell anybody about this, understand?"

We nod.

When we get to my house, Tommy and I get out and watch Victor's car disappear down the street, gunning through stop signs.

We don't say anything to each other. I give him the bag of weed and he walks home.

I walk inside and find a note from my mom saying she's out at the bar. I turn off the lights, sit down on the couch, and wait for the phone to ring.

Cold Comes in on the Feet of Black Birds

David Spiering

Somber winter sweeps forgotten [though] the woods
and I wonder for how much longer I'll remain
stationary between two hurricanes. There
was good food for me but I had to eat it off dirty plates—
I was on a train heading back east but first
we were going west to find the ultimate sums
of midnight numbers, blinded by vanity and shaded
by darkness and shadows. I
heard some woman say into her cell phone, "If
only you would've visited more often…" The
train started off slowly. I
felt like I was on an old brown boxcar. It's
tough to make quick sense when I'm draped
in booze and my good sense circuits [crackle]
with shorts. There
was more food served on dirty plates, but we're
"truckin." My
quicker sense is confused by all the motion
and my soul trembles like an icicle in the cold,
coming closer and closer to a [blessed] shatter.

Where My Father Stands

Sherri Levine

I'm standing in the yard
holding a rake. My
father calls my name,
Come here, he says.
With the tip of his pipe,
he points to a stack of
paper bags and gloves
lying on the garage
shelf. I'm afraid to go
inside the garage; I
might trip and fall on
the cracks, and get
bitten by a recluse.
Don't kill the spiders,
my father says, *They eat*
insects for lunch.
I don't know how I'm
going to fit all those
leaves into the paper
bags. A warm wind picks
up. A whirlwind of
dust and willow leaves

twirl until they
drop. I ask my father if
he's ever seen leaves
dance like that? I turn to
see if he's watching.
He's already gone.

The Fledgling

Birch Dwyer

Today on the phone with your mother, you
on your kitchen stool and she
in bed at a care facility, she demands

a report from your day, a pleasant packaging
of news from the front. Though her body is under siege,
though she can't remember

the name of your son, she is still
the queen demanding achievement for the crown.
Her voice towers from a throne of crumpled sheets.

So tell me, what did my amazing and talented daughter do today?

This is no time to let a mother down, yet
you explain, with no embellishment
that you fiddled with a few poems, did your hip exercises

and walked the dogs through a field of mud.
Your truth-telling hangs in the air
like a note off-key.

That's it, Mom. That's all I got.

Her tumbler of tea stamps the bedtable
with an audible thump, a scepter for news that does not please.
I wish we could just have a conversation, you say.

The comment lands on the bare floor
of the hospital room like a young hawk
trying to gain its footing against slick tile.

Twelfth Month

Andrea Campbell

It's a Thursday just past 5 p.m.,
three days away from when last year
you started on your
final, and most lonely, journey.

I have to pull these words out
like a heavy pail of water up
a long, long well.
What good is it to me to
be a poet when
you are the poem
and you're gone?

And yet—
the night turns into day
no matter how I struggle through it.
Fall turns brilliant red and yellow
whether I remember you or not.
Your children and my other child
remain, regardless of the space
you occupied that now is filled
with only memories and grief.

So I will reach for every tiny joy I can,
each blessed touch from those I love
and those who love me,
all the miracles that can be felt at any moment
of my days, and I will let the sadness of your leaving go
and hold you gladly in my heart forever.

Seeds of Doubt

David Langlinais

It had gotten so that Carol and her husband were themselves in tears, when not fighting back their emotions in an effort to put on strong faces. From the moment they'd arrived at the hospital they wanted the nurses and doctors, even the receptionist, to help their daughter. The little girl was obviously in pain. She'd been crying the whole time. The receptionist asked them to fill out forms, asked them if they had insurance, even asked them if they were in Lafayette on vacation, like that might have had something to do with the little girl's inability to urinate. It was five in the morning and everyone looked ready for their shifts to end. No one seemed to feel the urgency Carol and her husband did.

A young man sitting in the waiting room looked drunk and in pain. His hand, wrapped in what looked like toilet paper, bled in spots. He sat with a girl who also looked drunk and half asleep. She'd probably driven the injured boy to the hospital, maybe from a fraternity party. No one seemed in a hurry to help him either.

After a long while, a nurse led Carol and her husband and the little girl to a small room. The nurse said a doctor would see them shortly. Now in the little room, Carol and her husband reassured their daughter that everything would be okay, even though they didn't know for sure that it would be. No one had reassured them of anything. Another nurse came in and offered the girl a packet of crayons and a few pages torn from a coloring book, but the girl wasn't interested in coloring. She just wanted to pee. Carol's husband stood there quiet, brooding. His eyes raw. He looked the way he always did when their daughter was in any kind of pain. Like any of the times Carol took their daughter to the doctor for a barrage of scheduled shots and made him go along.

A moment later a doctor came in. She looked young for a doctor, probably right out of school, Carol couldn't be sure. Wearing clean pink scrubs, she appeared fresh, even at that hour of the morning. She had a kind face that put Carol at ease. Carol was glad it wasn't a male doctor. Her own gynecologist was a woman. Carol had always been more comfortable seeing women doctors, so could only assume her daughter felt the same way, even though only four years old.

"You poor little thing," the doctor said, putting on a compassionate face. "What's the matter?"

"We think she has a urinary tract infection," Carol said. "It hurts her when she pees and now we can't get her to pee at all. We don't know if she just doesn't want to or if there's something blocking it up."

"Can we do something to help her use the bathroom?" Carol's husband said.

Carol recognized her husband's tone. He was about to lose it if someone didn't do something to help their daughter.

"Her stomach is distended," Carol thought to add, "so we think it's backed up. We wonder how long she's been holding it in."

"Let's remove her shorts and panties," the doctor said. "Then I'll take a look."

Carol and her husband did as the doctor instructed. Then they had to hold the little girl down because she was crying and kicking hysterically, even though the doctor hadn't touched her yet.

"How long has she had the pain when urinating?" the doctor said, peering between the girl's legs. She gently pushed aside the fold of skin and took a quick look before the girl was able to force her knees back together.

"Well, it started last week, actually," Carol said. "We took her to her doctor in New Orleans and they took a urine sample and a culture, but it came back negative."

"Uh-huh," the doctor said. She pressed a hand on the little girl's swollen lower belly and the girl's crying became a scream. The doctor stopped pushing. "What's this here," the doctor said, pointing at a large bruise on the girl's inner thigh.

"I hadn't noticed that before," Carol said.

"She got it playing with her cousins," Carol's husband said to the doctor. Then, to Carol, he said, "You know that spinning toy they were playing on yesterday? The one you sit on and spin yourself? She must've got her thigh caught, because it pinched her real good."

"Uh-huh," the doctor said, no longer looking at the little girl, but instead looking at Carol and her husband. "Has she had any fever associated with all this?" she said. "Has there been any vomiting? Has she been listless, inactive...?"

"No, no," Carol said. "She's been fine. We're in town visiting family and she's been playing hard with her cousins. She's been normal except for when she has to pee. Now there's the pain and she can't seem to go at all. She's all distended."

"Do you have her in daycare?" the doctor said. "Or is she ever out of your care at any other time?"

"She goes to pre-school during the day," Carol said. "Other than that, no, she's always with us."

Carol's husband nodded.

The doctor hesitated. Then she said, "I don't want to alarm you, but I have to ask this: could there be any reason to suspect sexual abuse?"

Carol wasn't sure, but the doctor seemed to direct the question toward her husband. When Carol looked at him she could see his eyes welling up.

"What?" Carol's husband said.

"Why would you ask that?" Carol said to the doctor.

Her husband turned away from the doctor. He looked at Carol and said, "All her teachers are women, right? I mean the only man there is her drama teacher and he's gay."

"Why would you ask that?" Carol repeated, looking at the doctor. "I mean she's had bladder infections before. Why couldn't it just be that this time? At worst, we thought it was a urinary tract infection."

"I just don't want to rule anything out," the doctor said. "And if she had a urine culture only a week ago and it came back negative, then it raises some questions. Those tests are pretty thorough. They might miss something on occasion, but it's not likely."

"Are there janitors that we don't know about," Carol's husband said, his mind still at their daughter's school. His eyes continued to water and Carol wondered if he might cry. "She's never with anyone else but us," he added. "She's always happy and having a good time when I pick her up."

"My husband picks her up from school every day at 3:30," Carol told the doctor, for some reason feeling it necessary to explain.

"Could it be that drama teacher?" Carol's husband said.

"Look," the doctor said, "let's not get ahead of ourselves, okay? I probably should've waited till after the test to even bring it up."

Carol and her husband didn't say anything.

"Anyway," the doctor said, "we'll be giving her a catheter in a minute and then we'll get a sample. We'll have the test results about an hour after that. Then we'll know what we're dealing with. Until then, let's just keep her as comfortable as we can. She's not going to like the catheter, but it'll be quick and she'll feel much better when it's over."

The doctor had planted the idea in Carol's mind and it was hard getting it out of her head.

Four people came into the room—two woman in colorful scrubs and two big men—all slipping their hands into tight-fitting latex gloves. Being in an emergency center at five in the morning, they'd clearly grabbed anyone they could find to help out. One of the men also had on colorful scrubs, but the other had on a Medivac jacket. Carol remembered the helicopter she'd seen outside on the helipad when they'd first arrived.

The four hospital workers positioned themselves around the table, not seeming certain how to go about it. They might have been more comfortable dealing with mangled automobile accident victims than little girls who needed help urinating. Then they went into action as the two men, each holding a thigh, pried the girl's legs open. One woman swabbed rust-colored antiseptic around the girl's middle area, while the other readied the catheter. Carol held her daughter's head down while her husband held the girl's arms tightly over her head. The little girl screamed. Carol looked at her husband, looked at his eyes, and saw that he was crying.

"Okay, hold her still," the nurse guiding the catheter said, like they weren't already holding her down. The little girl began bucking and everyone tightened their grip. When the catheter hit home it was as if lancing a water balloon and the nurse with the sample cup seemed caught off guard. She fought to catch the urine that shot out much harder and more profusely than she'd anticipated, soaking everyone in urine.

"There it is," the nurse with the catheter said triumphantly, her sleeves soaked.

"That's it, sweetheart," one of the men said, a tall, hulking Cajun nurse with a pony tail. "*Cher, bébé,* get it all out, now. That's a good girl."

Once the urine had stopped and the catheter was removed, everyone stepped back from the table. The nurse with the cup held up the sample, only about an inch showing. Her rubber gloves soaked, they were no longer white and powdery, but shiny and transparent.

"Will that be enough for a sample?" Carol said, amazed that that was all the nurse had managed to catch in the flood of urine. Carol hoped they wouldn't have to go through it all over again to get more.

The four hospital staffers left the room. An old Hispanic woman came in with a bucket smelling of disinfectant. She mopped and cleaned the table and the floor before leaving, never saying a word. Now Carol and her husband sat alone with their daughter in the room again. The little girl wasn't crying for the first time in three hours. She sat on her father's lap sucking her thumb. Limp, exhausted, sleepy. Carol looked at her daughter, she looked at her husband holding her.

The same big men and two women came into the room again. They wore new scrubs and were dry now except for the Medivac man whose jacket and pants were still damp in places. They all put on fresh latex gloves. When the doctor came in she said she'd have to get another look, a better look than she'd been able to get when the little girl had fought her before the catheter. Everyone took the positions they'd had a moment earlier, like the time before had only been a rehearsal for something far more difficult. But the girl seemed relaxed now. She allowed the doctor to check her without anyone having to hold her down. Carol was proud of her daughter for being so brave. Everyone appeared relieved. The four helpers removed their gloves and turned to leave. Carol's husband thanked them for all their help, like they were strangers off the street and not hospital employees doing their job.

"Okay, she looks good," the doctor said.

Carol wasn't sure what she meant. "So then it *is* a urinary tract infection?" she said.

"We won't know that until the lab report comes back," the doctor said. "Just hang tight and I'll let you know as soon as we know anything."

Carol and her husband sat alone with their daughter in the little room again. They hadn't said anything for a while. Then Carol said, "Why would she say that?"

"It isn't that," her husband said. "So stop thinking about it. I can't believe she'd even say that. It's goddamn irresponsible."

"Still, why would she say it?" Carol said.

"Maybe she has to," he said. "It's a public hospital, so maybe they're required by law to ask certain questions."

Carol looked at her husband, maybe with an incredulous face, because he said, "Hell, I don't know, Carol. You don't think I'm as floored by all this as you are? I mean, goddamn."

Carol watched her husband rock the little girl who now looked drained from the trauma. She sucked the thumb of the same hand that clutched the little pillow that had been her binky from the time she was six-months old.

"I'm gonna kill that goddamn drama teacher," Carol's husband said, teary eyed again. "The fucking freak." His jaw muscles flexed, his eyes continued watering up and he sounded like he meant it.

"He's gay, Peter," Carol said with a wide-eyed look that told her husband she didn't approve of that kind of language in front of their daughter. "That doesn't automatically make him a pedophile." As she said it, though, she realized she didn't know if it were true. She'd met the man—a tall, pasty, doughy-looking man. He seemed harmless. He was effeminate in a way that is threatening to men, but not women. For some reason, it would've been far more peculiar having a straight man teaching at a pre-school. Teaching drama, of all things.

"Then who else could it be?" her husband said.

"We don't even know if that's what it is yet," Carol said. "I mean the doctor sounded sorry she brought it up." She reached for her daughter's foot. When Carol ran her fingernails across the sole of the foot, the girl jerked it away playfully. Then Carol took hold of the little foot again. She didn't tickle it this time, but held it so that she could see her daughter's inner thigh. She wanted to get a better look at the bruise.

"How did she get this again?" Carol said.

Her husband sat staring at the far wall, stewing. "What?" he said.

"Was I around when she got this?" Carol said.

"I don't know," he said, now looking at the bruise. "You were probably in the kitchen or outside on the patio with everyone. I was in the playroom with the girls when it happened. It wasn't a big deal. She didn't even cry that much."

"I'm just surprised I never saw it, that's all."

Carol's husband didn't say anything. A moment later he changed the subject. "Are there any janitors there?" he said.

"I don't know," Carol said, thinking they'd already ruled out the school.

They sat quiet again and Carol thought about their daily lives. They led a simple life, were hopelessly routine-oriented. Every day the same: They got up. He packed their daughter's lunchbox and fed her breakfast before going out on the front porch to play. Meanwhile, Carol showered and dressed for work. Then they all left the house together, he in his car, Carol in hers with the little girl. Carol dropped her off at school on the way to work. He worked as a freelance photographer, so had the flexibility to pick up their daughter at 3:30 most days. Then he'd call Carol to let her know where they were. From the park if they were there, or from the house. Carol would get home around six and then they'd have dinner. After that they might go outside with glasses of wine to watch their daughter play in the front yard before her bath.

Outside of school, their daughter was never alone with anyone but her husband. Carol had to stop her mind from going where it was starting to go. It made her sick thinking it. She couldn't believe she were even entertaining the idea. She had to question everything about herself. But she couldn't help it. Now she questioned everything about her husband. She'd read or heard somewhere—maybe she'd seen it on TV—that when women found out their husbands were sexually abusing their children the women always said they'd never suspected a thing. Then, in hindsight, the women realized it had been right there in front of them the whole time; that they must have been in denial, because they never saw the obvious. Carol stopped herself from thinking about it any further. "Let's just wait for the test results, okay?" she said.

Carol's husband sat brooding and didn't say anything. He looked ready to kill someone. He was still fixated on the school, she thought. Or was he? What was he really thinking? For a second Carol felt she didn't know him at all anymore and, again, she had to push the thought from her mind.

Dark River, Wings of Glass

Umpqua Community College, October 1, 2015

Nancy Nowak

i.

Evening. Breath
held at the heart, exhaled

as three sounds, three times
meant to be

what is gone, current, yet to come
interwoven

Recognize the light

across the darkened campus
in the pebbled walkways'
slick shine, luminous blades

of grass holding onto summer

while across the river, unseen
from here

on a balcony
hums a dim light
that might be mistaken
for a monitor tracking a heart.

ii.
Night is gone, breath
now shadowed
by its cruelest echo.

No matter how
we try turning back
the sounds

into something
recognizable, cannon fire
frightening crows from a field
into flight

they run toward us, those who can
their ragged breath telling us

crouch in some darkened space or
behind a stone retaining wall.

Except the room where

why would anyone
how could you think
what else could be done as

the air is torn & torn & torn
the inverse of breath resounding.

iii.
In each day after
is the same day, unyielding.

See us move

like stones or as though
we'd swallowed darkness

across fenced grass, along
aggregate paths

yet if we are stone

how can we

breathe. The sky
so filled with light

it forces shut our eyes

has not hardened, nor
have our hearts, unmended.

The weight we feel
though emptied

into each of us
becomes no easier to bear.

iv.
Should we step from sorrow's
meadowed bank into the first circle

they recognize
why we have come

to them, the dogs'
golden heads lifting slightly
toward our approach.

Unwavering, they lie at points
of a compass rose

as though their lives were spent

forever in longing

for us to kneel
beside them, pour our grief
like blessings upon them

as though they never
will leave us

until they are led away

v.
Sorrow flows into
the sounded lament

two rivers only
able to recall

as though each name
derives from the insistent
voice in its current
always escaping

but we have learned *river*
means what cannot be moved

from, the place alongside
that must watch

where we remain.

vi.

North and South form one grieving
river, long called *bring across*

as though we could
gather in our arms all nine

like a spray of flowers
enfolded in our embrace, their vessel.

Instead we gather
for them, *on a hill far away*, an overlook
above rapids, in unrelenting
rain, uncertain sun. Gone

we want them
still: captive

in roses pinned to blackness, a solitary
ivory turned the color of rust
eight red ones darkening;

in tesserae: blue river, meadow green, red
sky in morning: transformed

into dragonflies, as though nine
had landed lightly
there, on the retaining

wall, bearing in that lightness
some word for us.

vii.
Luminous, veined
wings bear the long body

sometimes called *darning needle*
as though by its weaving flight

the jagged sky, our
hearts, all that was cut

could be mended.

Then a dry sound, like breath
caught in the throat:

the rustle of paper
cranes, a thousandfold, peaceful

flight suspended
just above us until
we must see them

off. Blameless, they are forced
to migrate from hurt
to terrible hurt, impart

some sense of our losses

trusting they will come
at last to rest.

Good Fruit, Bad Fruit

Judith DeVilliers

Job, the troubled master-chef, sat in ashes
gobbling down a huge piece of fruit pie
he made from the tree of knowledge
of good and evil that grew in the garden.

His friends Eliphaz, Bildad and Zophar
heard of his troubles and came quickly
to join him in this feast, as they all
brewed the fruit into creative concoctions.

They sat around Job with the juice
of the fruit oozing out of their mouths,
thick and redder than blood, each
sharing his recipe for this special fruit.

They discussed its use for fruit smoothies,
sweet & sour jams, pies, and tarts all made from
the fruit of the tree of knowledge cultivated
in orchards and even grown wild in forests.

Then Job heard God's voice softly in a wind
that finally increased into a tornado, ripping
through his orchard, uprooting and
utterly destroying every tree.

Finally Job saw God—and repented.

Formations

Greg Nicholl

Caught on the wrong side of the dam's blueprint,
a tribe is displaced, the land redlined.

Architects divert streams, call it advancement.
It's easy to pretend boundaries never existed

if you really want to. Settlements submerged
house by house beneath murky lagoons

where their foundations are mistaken for creatures
that lurk in darkness. On clear days, you can see

the entrance of the town hall, walls of a saloon,
a school yard with an abandoned orchard out back.

On the other side of the dam, in another town,
boys float toy soldiers in Styrofoam cups,

leave them overnight to freeze, their plastic bodies
suspended in cylinders of ice, a lineup they dub

Chernobyl. The ice so clear it reveals tiny green men
who stand ready to attack invisible armies

that approach from all sides. Anything to protect
their land from hostile takeover.

And when the temperature rises and they dive
into the lake, they forget the town beneath,

their feet barely grazing the top of the church spire
as they dip below the surface to swim to the other side.

What She Told Her Family About Her New Life

Vivienne Popperl

*for my grandmother, who emigrated from Eastern Europe
to Southern Africa in her twenties, with gratitude*
                    —after Li-Young Lee's *A Dove*! I Said

A rose, she said.
What she meant was a thicket.
What she meant was dusty earth.

A mountain blue-bird, she said.
What she meant was a store-room's barred windows.
What she meant was shelves of canned goods, sacks of flour.

A wide green meadow, she said.
What she meant was the smell of carbolic soap.
What she meant was scratching ciphers on a yellowed page.

A gold ring, she said.
What she meant was raw knuckles.
What she meant was chapped lips.

A cradle, she said.
What she meant was a kitchen table.
What she meant was a midwife between her legs.

Tiny silk stitches, she said.
What she meant was a goat cart to carry her children to school.
What she meant was a shotgun to defend them.

Blue silk and feathers, she said.
What she meant was a widow's black gabardine.
What she meant was a twisted rope.

Fire, she said.
What she meant was curled fingers poking through woolen gloves.
What she meant was hands smudged by coal.

Fire, red flush of shame
heart burnt by grief;
Fire's single flame slants in the darkened doorway.

Fire lights the belly,
scours the heart.
Fire flares, spends itself in ashes.

What she should have said was:
flames of bitterness.

What I want to say to her is:
fierce brave heart left behind
you arose from the ashes.

1-in-4

Alicia Schmidt

—For the strong women who raised me.
May I be half as impressive.

"Just relax..."

I wake from what feels like a nightmare, push my head off the pillow and scoop a wild mass of red hair off my face. It isn't a natural kind of red; it's more of a cherry red you can only get out of a black jar with gory lettering spelling the name of a brand that doesn't sound like it has much to do with hair dye. The name of the color is something like "rocker chick" or "cherri bomb." I honestly can't remember, but I like it. It suits me. My body is exhausted even though I just woke up. Everything hurts. Perching on the edge of my bed, I grab a hair-tie from the nightstand and pull the unruly mass of cascading waves into a crooked ponytail. I take a deep breath and look up, across the room, at my reflection in the mirror I have propped up against the wall.

"Well, it could be worse." I mumble. I'm surprised the curls managed to hold overnight. I am so keeping that hairspray.

I stand up and my legs feel weak and stiff, like I ran a marathon or something. I stumble to the bathroom and, grabbing a makeup wipe, begin to scrub the smeared mascara from under my eyes. It must have been quite a night if I forgot to take off my makeup. I wince as the chemicals sink into an open cut.

> *"Hey! Get off her, you son of a bitch!" Someone was yelling. I heard a chaos of footsteps, felt arms lifting me from the pavement.*

The memories come in discombobulated flashes of things that don't seem possible. I stare into the bathroom mirror waiting for the story behind the split lip and bruised cheekbone.

Nothing seems real anymore.

My head hurts, my muscles shake when I move, I don't recognize the girl in the mirror.

"How did she get so beat to hell?" I wonder as tears well up in her blue eyes. I feel the hot sting behind my own eyes and know her tears must be mine. A tear runs over the cut on her lip and mine begins to burn.

Nothing makes sense.

Nothing will connect.

Why is she crying?

Why am *I* crying?

"I need coffee," I mumble, swiping the tears from under my eyes. The girl in the mirror does the same.

Away from the mirror girl, my mind turns to breakfast. "Eggs... yeah, with potatoes or something." I mumble, trying to verbally make sense of things.

I walk down the hallway piled with books and down the wrought-iron stairs, tripping on another pile of books and sending CD cases clattering to the floor. I walk through the sparsely furnished main room, with a makeshift table that used to be the travel case of a large kick drum. Crumpled papers are strewn across the floor.

They had been thrown.

Last night. I remember now, Colin had thrown them...or I threw them at Colin.

"Why can't I remember anything?" I hold my head in my hands, pressing my eyes into the palms. Breathe. "It doesn't matter." I lie, shaking my head like the physical act could help shake the memories loose from my brain.

Slowly, I take the two steps into the kitchen and fill the coffee pot with water so I can get it brewing. I grab a potato out of the basket by the stove and wash it in the small sink before grabbing a knife and dicing it up for an omelet, not bothering to get a cutting board out. With breakfast finally cooking I stare into the black void of the filling coffee pot and watch the percolation—mind roving absently, gone and present, and watching, always watching the slow trickling of the bitter life juice.

We had a show last night...

The high-pitched beep of the coffee pot pierces my ears. I pull a pink octopus mug from the cupboard above the pot and pour coffee into the one of many novelty mugs in my possession. I lean against the kitchen counter and stare out the large windows that dominate the outer wall of my drafty apartment.

"Come on Eddie!" Colin was yelling at me from the door, "We'll be late!"

"I'm coming!" I hollered back and hopped out of my room still struggling with the zipper on a black combat boot.

"Ok, I'm ready, I'm ready. Where's my guitar?"
"In the car. Let's go."

"Ow!" I croak as coffee burns the cut on my lip. My voice sounds hoarse, like I had been screaming. But more than that, my neck hurts, and not in a head-banging-injury kinda way.

I set the mug on the counter and run a hand gingerly across my neck. I feel the familiar pain of a bruise, but it's not just in one spot. Which seems to rule out a hickey.

I get a sinking feeling in my stomach like it knows the story my head can't remember.

The acrid stench of burning Teflon and food curls up my nose, "What's burning?"

I scurry across the kitchen and pull the pan of now blackened potatoes off the stovetop. "Damn it." But, on second look it seems fine, so I crack a few eggs into the pan and rush to scramble them before they get too cooked, honestly, just hoping for the best. I burn almost everything I've ever tried to cook—which is only a problem when I bother to try and feed other people. Actually, I'm kind of fond of the smoky blackened flavor of my culinary creations.

I take another gulp of coffee and wince from the pain.

"How the...?"

I know one of these days all those hours watching YouTube tutorials will pay off. I take a deep breath and swing the pan gently in preparation for my latest flip attempt. My arms hurt and they shake slightly from holding the weight. Finally, I make my move to flip and the loosely formed egg-cake immediately crumbles. No surprise, honestly. Shrugging I get cheddar out of the 'fridge and sprinkle it on the crumbled mess. I manage to slide it onto a plate without making a mess, and the burned potato taste is barely noticeable. So my imaginary food critics can suck it.

> *"Don't touch me! Dammit! Let me go!" I shrieked, kicking and screaming feebly...I felt suffocated.*
>
> *"Eddie! Shut up would you! I'm trying to help you!"*
>
> *I finally managed to land a kick before tumbling onto the floor.*
>
> *"Leave me alone!" Desperate for something to put space between us, I grabbed the stack of papers off the drum case table and threw them...*

A flash of pain once again startles me from the memory.

My hip had caught the corner of the counter as I absentmindedly tried to make my way out of the kitchen towards the couch. Glaring at the offending corner, I notice a large blackish-mauve bruise fully fleshed out on my outer thigh. A sharp pain in my ribs points to more bruising. It seems the more I wake up, the more injuries I find.

I set down the now empty plate and lift my baggy Blink-182 shirt to examine my now dappled blue and white torso in the poor reflection of the TV screen. I have to get weirdly close to the old screen to see the definition of the bruises, and even then, the image is distorted.

Standing there I can't bring myself to believe that they are real.

I stretch the shirt back down over my hips and make my way back to my abandoned coffee mug in the kitchen. A poke to a hand shaped bruise on my arm tells me they are, in fact, quite real and not some elaborate body paint hoax. Why it would be a body paint hoax I don't know, but it's the only thing I can come up with that doesn't involve getting beaten half to death.

The coffee seems to be clearing the fog.

"Hey, it's Edith, isn't it?" A heavy guy with bad tattoos approached as I was manning the merch table in the back of the concert venue.

"Most people call me Eddie." I said. "Anything look good to you? The shirts are twenty, hats twenty-five, posters and CD's are five bucks a piece, and we're giving away your choice of a sticker or button with any purchase of twenty bucks or more." I smiled and waited while he checked me out and then the merch, and then me again. Totally typical. I mentally rolled my eyes. Some guys. But I was used to it, so I put on my best customer service face and waited.

"You know you sing well." He leered at me with what I could only assume he thought was his 'sexy look.'

"So I've been told. Thanks." I smiled back politely, trying not to laugh.

"I didn't know girls could play the guitar like that."

"Girls can do a lot of things now. We can even vote."

He forced a laugh and flicked the end of his nose with his thumb. "You're a funny girl, Eddie, I like you." He paused to stare.

"Soooo are ya gonna buy somethin'? Or what?" I could feel my patience evaporating.

"How much to take you out back and rock your world?" He smirked. "It wouldn't take very long, I'm good like that."

"Huh, right, yeah. I'm sure you are. It's just that I'm, uh, kinda busy right now, and, you know, actually, my world's pretty rockin' without you screwin' things up. So, you and your good friend Righty can go have a good time without me. ah-kay? BYE." I smiled and waved him off.

"Fat bitch."

"I know."

"I was gonna buy something."

"No, I don't think you were." Colin's voice rang out behind me. He had appeared from backstage in his typical ninja-like silence.

"Thanks for the assist, but I think I had him under control." I turned around and leaned into his arm, a crooked smirk on my face.

Colin pushed me back onto my feet and chuckled, "I'm sure you did." He was almost a foot taller than my perfectly respectable five-foot-three and a hundred pounds heavier, with massive shoulders. It's not that he was obese or anything, just big and muscular. With one hand he swept his artificially silver bangs back off his face. "So, there's an after-party thing going on down stairs, seems kinda lame, but we should prob'ly go for a bit. On the up-side—free booze for the band...whadda ya think?"

"Hangovers need water." I mumble as I snap back to reality. Someone had said that to me last night, but I don't remember who. I get up and walk over to the sink to fill the now empty mug with water. My body is tired and achy, and I can't keep standing. I shuffle over to the couch and flop down on its threadbare surface. The fabric scratchy against my skin.

"Make sure she drinks plenty of water, and then have her try and sleep. She's pretty banged up, but she'll be ok in a few weeks."

"Thanks doc." A male voice responded.

It was a familiar voice, I know that much. But all the memories are so foggy I can't place him.

"Hey, what's goin' on with you? I thought you said you were fine?"

"Well I'm not. OK?" I pulled away from him.

"Ok. Can I help you out of those—" He reached out to touch me and I pulled back.

Colin. I remember now. Or, at least, I think I do. Maybe. Everything is still so foggy. Colin had attacked me. No. Well...NO. The more I think about last night the more none of it makes any sense. He was trying to get something off me—help me? He told me to relax. I don't remember taking my clothes off. I don't remember much of anything.

"Hey, hey, hey, relax, it's ok." Colin whispered reaching out for me once again.

"I can't relax. Please don't ask me to relax." I sobbed quietly as he slowly removed the ruined clothes and carried me upstairs.

"I- I can't...I d-don't...I-I ca-can't—I can't re-" I stammered through heaving sobs.

"Shhh, shh, it's gonna be ok. You're safe now. You're safe now."

I fidget restlessly. I can't seem to get comfortable. Every movement hurts something else. I pick at the loose threads of the couch trying not to think about anything too hard. Every part of me seems tense even though it hurts. It hurts to breathe and I try to remember what they told me about panic attacks.

I need to calm down.

Breathe in...

Touch something.

Breathe out...

See something.

Breathe in...

Hear something.

"You sure have some pretty strong opinions for someone who's wrong!" I yelled across the noise of the crowded bar.

"I just think Green Day was more influential on modern punk than Blink!" The stranger yelled back. The tight cords of muscle bulged out of his scrawny neck.

"Yeah, but that's not the only blatantly wrong opinion you've expressed tonight!" I yelled back slamming another empty bar glass on the table.

"Oh yeah? And wha' gives you the righ' to decide my opinions are wrong?" He slurred swaying dangerously close to me.

This was gonna be good.

"I write for that magazine you're oh so fond of referencing. You even referenced one of my reviews."

And now came my favorite part of the conversation.

"No way. All the writers are dudes." He said with all the authority of one too many beers.

"Hi, I'm Eddie Ross. It's short for Edith. I'll let you fig-ure that out at your own pace." I sucked an ice cube into my mouth and waited as it clicked across my teeth.

"YOU'RE EDDIE ROSS? YOU'RE A GIRL! I love your reviews. Eddie Ross is a girl…" He trailed off into silence.

I continued to suck on ice cubes and watched the show that was now playing out on his face. His booze addled brain desperately trying to sort through the new information. Don't laugh. I reminded myself.

"Eddie Ross huh?" He mumbled looking at me.

"In the flesh." I smiled and spread my arms with a dra-matic flourish.

"Damn fine flesh if I do say so m'self." He winked.

"Huh." I quickly sucked another ice cube into my mouth to avoid having to give a real answer.

Silence hung heavy between us. Things had taken a weird turn I wasn't sure how to navigate.

"So, Eddie…would you want to, uh, maybe, go out sometime?" He asked.

"What?" I said as more of a reflex than a real question. "I mean, I don't really go out with strangers."

I should have said something to soften the blow…Should have made an excuse…Should have lied…Said I was with someone…Any-thing…To spare his feelings…My fault.

I did this.

I feel my eyes burn and know I'm crying.

Breathe in…

Hear.

"Let me at least buy you a drink or something." He looked up at me with a fresh kind of light in his eyes.

"Band members drink for free tonight." I reminded him.

"I don't care. Whad're ya drinkin?" He pushed.

"Whiskey sour." I rolled my eyes and let him walk off to the bar. "With Jameson please!" I called after. If he was going to pay, I could finally get something better than well whiskey.

I force myself off the couch. I need more water...Colin told me to drink water...I have to drink plenty of water...I drag my feet across the cold floor to the sink and fill my cup again.

Why do I always drink too much too quickly? Why? What's wrong with me?

I'm gonna have to pee so bad later...The bathroom is upstairs... I don't know if I can get back up the stairs. I can't even walk.

Breathe out...

See.

"Are you friends with the bartender or something?" My fanboy said as he returned with the drinks.

It seemed like it had taken him a long time to get the drinks, but I didn't really care.

"Yeah, he's a friend. I do a lot of reviews of shows here. So we talk a lot afterwards." I grabbed the fresh drink off the table and took a gulp. Something tasted off. Like the bartender was using old sour mix or something.

"You do anything besides write reviews?" He asked casually.

"*Yeah, I work at a bar.*" *I took another drink.*

"*So you bartend?*" *His sudden interest in getting to know me seemed kind of strange.*

"*Nah, cocktail.*" *I finished the drink.* "*The m-money is uuusssually…b-better.*"

"*Still, that mus' be an in'eresting gig. Right? You probably meet tons of different people.*" *He grabbed my hand and I noticed the muscles in his arm writhing. His grip felt like it could break my fingers…*

"*Ow!*"

"*How you feelin' baby? You had a lot to drink.*" *All three of his smiling faces leaned in close to me.*

"*Whathfuiwrnwi-*" *I tumbled off my stool and he grabbed me.*

"*Don't worry Eddie. I'm gonna take care of you…*"

The crash of breaking pottery startles me from the memories. Cold water splatters across my feet and ankles as the mug shatters on the floor. "Damn, I like that mug." My hands were shaking. Are shaking. I kneel on the floor to clean up the mess, but I'm such a wreck I can barely pick up the pieces of ceramic. I don't feel much like making my usual sarcastic comments at the broken pottery.

My head hurts. I release the wild tangle of hair from its ponytail prison. I don't know if I want to remember anymore.

Breathe in…

Touch.

He was kissing me. It hurt. I didn't like it.

"*You have beautiful hair baby,*" *he whispered in my ear, taking hold of a fistful. "It's what drew me to you. That wild beautiful hair.*"

I could feel his hot breath on my skin. Feel his hand groping beneath my skirt.

"*Stop, please, stop. Please—*" *But my words were a slurred mumble. I tried to push him off, but my arms wouldn't move. Tried to kick but my legs were heavy.*

"*Wha-? You're a tough one arenchya?*" *His hand tightened in my hair ripping chunks out by the root.*

"*No! Stop!*" *My voice had more strength this time. I managed to swing my arm up and land a smack to his left ear.*

"*What the fuck! You little bitch!*"

I swung both arms wildly, trying…trying…"*Help…*" *I managed to gasp.*

"*Oh? Ya got some life left in ya? Huh? I can take care of that.*" *He clamped both hands around my throat,* "*Just relax…*"

"I." *Gasp.* "WILL NOT." *Gasp.* "RELAX."

The words fight their way out of my shaking torso.

I push myself off the damp floor. Hot salt-water drops fall from my eyes and mix with the red water dripping from the tangled ends of my hair. "Why this hair?"

It looks like I died.

"Why? Should've been black…or something…anything…Why did I choose this wild mess of hair?" Sobbing, I grab handfuls of it by the roots and try to rip it out.

The hair is too strong.

"NO!"

I. Need. It. GONE.

I drag myself to my feet and grab the scissors from the drawer by the stove.

You weak little bitch.

I can hear the slur of his voice creeping through my ears.

My legs shake with every step as I crawl my way up the stairs to the bathroom.

My wild-haired beauty.

I stare into the mirror at the hair that had been my downfall.

That girl inside looks like a ghost. That girl with the pale skin contrasting bruised black. That girl with the eyes made of crystallized pain. Pupil-less. Ringed in blood.

Lifeless.

Deftly I take hold of a chunk of hair and raise the scissors to it—the mirror girl does the same.

Hesitation. The blades stick as I try to force them closed.

You'll never be strong enough.

The satisfying slice rings in my ears—the sound of vengeance.

Each wave falls heavy past the shoulders of the girl in the mirror, brushing my arm. Before I know it the wild animal of hair is separated from her scalp—my scalp—lying dead on the bathroom floor.

I feel lighter.

The pounding of my headache begins to diminish. I take the razor from the shower and run it over the patchy stubble of my scalp.

Mine.

A whisper, "no."

I force myself to try and recognize the mirror girl. I examine every curve of her lips, every freckle, every cut and bruise. The longer I stare, the less I recognize until I'm forced to look away from her cold eyes.

I strip yesterday's clothes from my body—the aching flesh mocks me. Carefully I step into the center of the bathtub-shower combo and turn on the water.

The icy rain pelts my flesh. And yet I feel nothing.

I turn the water temperature to all the way up. The cold slowly turns hot enough to freeze.

My skin turns red. And yet I feel nothing.

I curl in on myself, sinking down to place forehead to knees, ankles to hips.

Water blocks my nose and mouth. I wish it would rise up and drown me.

Breathe in…

Calm.

I extend my legs until my feet reach the end of the tub and lean back so that my spine fits the curvature and my head rests on the hard, smooth edge. I close my eyes.

Breathe out…

Hear something.

I listen to the soft rhythm of the shower on the ceramic, and the strange slap of the water as it hits the plastic shower curtain.

Breathe in...

Feel something.

Eyes closed I bid my body find a pulse. I think about my fingertips, callus from guitar, pressing into the textured base of the tub.

Breathe out...

Find strength.

As the hot water seeps into my bones and the blood vessels dilate, I begin to feel the soft thrum of a pulse beneath my skin. I allow my mind to follow that pulse up my arms and through my body. It rushes to the rawness of my scalp and down the muscles of my legs to my toes. I wiggle them and feel the pulse strengthen. Faster. Coursing through my body to my heart—pounding in my chest.

My heart.

My body.

41.

Geoff Cannard

In awe I looked upon the ocean first,
a boy struck dumb by all uncircumscribed,
and long I stood without the proffered thirst,
resenting all the drink to be imbibed.
When bold as youth commands I splashed into
the vomitous solution with my peers,
an evidence abundantly in view
concealed realizations of my fears.
And as, and though, we drank as all we must
and pissed and spewed the liquid right back up,
submerged we all ignored our old disgust,
hid insufficient to the ocean's cup.
And I the sea have too well understood
in knowing understanding does no good.

Eschatology

Jack Eikrem

in the science-fiction glow
of the bugzapper moths
dancing above me
i light a cigarette
it's the last cowboy killer
      the one
        i always turn
        over for luck after
        smacking the end of the pack
        with the heel of my hand
        and tearing off
        the silver
as i drag
the orange coal
at the end of the barrel
burns
like Mars
or an evil eye
in the dark of the porch
under the flickering bugzapper

and i taste bitter
parchment and the dry
bones of prophets
    how fragile the moths that fly in
    the night on their papery wings
    towards the light that will burn them
    back down to dust
i am flicking the last of the dust
from my cigarette butt
    i toss it somewhere
    out in the yard
    to gutter and die
        or will it kindle something

Insomnia Returns in Form of Labrys

Marisa P. Clark

Here is the labrys. It hangs
above the bed. From a hypnagogic fog,
its nicked blades whisper stories. Do not
mistake the streaks of blood for rust. Do not
turn on the light. On the nightstand, a litter
of letters—no need to reread. The woman who wrote
them, she was lying—to me, about me, sometimes
with/beside/abovebelowinside me. Do not
mistake her strokes of ink for promises
or plans. Do not confuse
her words of love
with love.

Here is the labrys. It hovers,
handle within reach. Its two blades flare
like the spread wings of a raptor diving to snatch
easy prey—or like two heads conjoined, two faces turned away:
a perfect portrait of her or of us, perhaps of them,
or of Janus, the Roman god of gateways,
time, and change, starts and—

Stop.

   Go to sleep.

labrys: *n., sing.* A ceremonial battle-axe wielded only by women; associated with Amazons and Minoan civilization; sometimes pictured in ancient artworks with the sacred bull's horns of consecration.

battle-axe: *n., pejorative* An angry, crone-aged woman. See also **harridan** and **harpy**, **termagant** and **virago** (this last a heroic and/or mannish woman).

Amazons: *Greek mythology* A nation of woman warriors, beloved among lesbians (AKA **dykes** AKA **bulldykes**).

labrys: *n., etc.* Emblem of lesbians, esp. @1970s–1980s; often seen tattooed on a burly woman's bicep or strung on a leather strap to swing between a braless bulldyke's breasts.

dyke AKA **bulldyke:** *n., and so forth,* and either *pejorative slang* or *badge of pride* for **lesbian**, depending on user and usage.

bull: *Astrology* Symbol for Taurus; reputed for virility, stubbornness, and reckless promenades through china shops. Animal selected for ritual sacrifice by women to the Moon Goddess.

labrys: *Etymology* Possible connection with **Labyrinth**, "House of the Double Axe" and home or prison to the Minotaur (AKA "Moon-Bull"), the monstrous progeny begotten when an unfaithful queen tricked a magnificent white bull into a lusty—

   Fuck.

      I'm wide awake.

For our first meal as lovers, she sliced
cauliflower, the first head I'd ever bought,

and muttered, as she always did, that my knives
weren't sharp enough. Still, she cut
such perfect pieces. I saw in each
a cross-section of a brain. She saw
the Tree of Life; she saw
a labyrinth. She was the one
who'd taught me the difference
between a labyrinth and a maze: the one
a site of meditation, with an unbroken path
to a destination; the other a puzzle of choices,
teases, and dead-ends. I've never
roasted cauliflower again.

Years before, we'd gotten lost
on a long walk in Louisville—
but is it fair to call us lost
when we had no goal? Two friends
on an adventure, we laughed all day.
And now I can't stop picturing how she leaned
into that great old oak, in the summer evening light,
and how its trunk enfolded her, her body supple
and trusting, just like at home, her smile hinting
of bravado as before she scores
a crushing Scrabble blow—and how she took
my hand and skipped ahead, urging me
toward the river, and in that instant
showed me how our life could be
if only—she let go

my hand,
        and I let go the thought

that haunts me now. As for the labrys—
I should take it down and whack away this phantom
that assails while somewhere else she sleeps grinding
her pretty teeth to splinters and dreams chewing
on the truth she eschews by day. But all
my slashing at thin air will come
to nothing—can't draw blood
from a ghost—and do I
really wish to kill her
memory or shred her
words, fairy tales
though they be? They're all
she left me. She left me. Cut me
off. I won't do the same to her.
As for the labrys—what if I leave it
hanging? To be left

       hanging
           is such an ugly fate.

My Shadow

Paulann Petersen

Come dusk, you will
unlatch yourself from me
and move on your own.
Come twilight, the shade you make
will become a *shade*, moving
wherever you please.

Let dusk do its half-light work
on me. It will loosen you
so you slip away
from the body of who I am.
A dark petal fallen from my bloom,
you'll let the breeze carry you along.
May you roam. Blue-black
bit of blossom.
My blank-dark self
the sun insists
be attached to me.

But sun has set. The rules
are changed. This is not light,

is not dark, but the partial
in between. You are my part
that can slip in beside
my dead and my living.
You can listen to them both.
Please take notes so you
can report back. Dusk
can last only so long,
darkness too. At dawn,
we reconvene.

When I Wouldn't Eat My Disgusting Liver

Sherri Levine

When I wouldn't eat my disgusting
liver my mother said I should be
grateful, *Children are starving in
Africa,* she'd say, dumping more
ketchup on my plate. When I was
sick and wanted broth my mother
told me it could be worse; I might be
dying of diphtheria. *You should be
grateful you have your health.*

When my husband left, she said she never really liked
him, that he was way too young for me.
I watched her pull back her wrinkles,
sighing into the rearview mirror.
*Look, you should be grateful that you are
still young and pretty.
I remember when you were a little girl
you used to dance in front of the stove;
you looked so happy*—When I started
losing my looks she said, *be grateful at
least you have your legs.* Recently, I lost
my job, *A slap in the face,* she said.

*Well, at least you have your
teeth,* she said pointing to her
implants—*These cost a fortune.*

Rum and Coke

Ace Boggess

In the state of West Virginia, you can't plead insanity due to drug addiction. Crimes you commit belong to you like a tattoo acquired while drunk. Nonetheless, when I shoved that man to the ground, held him there, and took his wallet, desperate and hoping for enough cash to buy some pills, I was insane. As I raced off to find my dealer so I could score and ease my suffering, I might as well have been Renfield gibbering and waiting for the master's return. There was no right or wrong to me; there was misery or calm.

Fourteen months later, after two stints in rehab and more twelve-step meetings than I could count or remember, I stood before the Cabell County Circuit Judge saner than I had been in almost a decade. With a clear head, I heard him sentence me to an indefinite term of five to eighteen years for strong-armed robbery. Sane, too, I went first to the Regional Jail in Barboursville, then the DOC intake facility in Martinsburg, before ending up at Boone County Correctional Center in Rock Haul, West Virginia—a town so small I had never heard, not even as home to a prison.

Mind right, I wore my khakis straight like a good soldier and walked slowly over the stone floors in my flimsy blue state-issued sneakers. I showered with my eyes open, played cards with clarity and certainty, worked in the kitchen with full awareness of every extra flake of cayenne pepper I added to the stew. When I smelled pages from the Bible burning in some back cell—not a Divine scent, but a rotten, earthly one like a trash fire—I knew I wasn't hallucinating, and that someone had wrapped tobacco in *Psalms* or maybe *Revelations*. When guards menaced me, using their hard voices and pinprick stares, I dreaded their genuineness, finding not a hint of paranoia on my part. And the beatings I took from other cons? I received each blow without a fuzzy thought to cushion me. Yes, sanity was the worst goddamned thing that ever happened to me.

I submitted a sick-call slip, went to medical, and asked the doc, "Can you make me crazy again?"

He laughed so hard his boozy breath hit my cheek from three feet away.

I advised my counselor, "I'm having problems. I think I'm too sane for this place."

She smiled, as friendly as anyone I met on the inside, and told me, "That's the punishment part of the program. Might as well learn to accept it."

Same with the chaplain who offered me Jesus, and also my cell-mates who said, "Go back to sleep."

Sleep *was* the best way to pass my time. It had enough of that comfortable lunacy to distract me, if only I could hold onto it when I woke. There were escapes through cemeteries, hiding in graves until guards and police dressed like infantry went by. There were cats that knew a map of the place and could lead a man out were he fast enough. I smelled things I hadn't smelled in years: Thanksgiving turkey, Christmas ham, oil from an engine, my soon-to-be ex-wife's perfume. I had many good times in that swirl of unreality, especially if I caught a nap on my bunk around noon. But then I awoke to the squawk of a guard's radio or the scent of a man on the shitter not ten feet away, and I wiped my eyes to be sure I wasn't crying.

Sometimes I tied a sock around my ears and eyes to erase the locked world and force myself back into that dopy dreamland. It rarely did any good. I was as sober as a steep cliff, straight as a fall, and as terrified of looking up as down.

I discussed these things with my counselor, the chaplain, and the doc, all of whom after a year or so finally decided I had lost my mind. "No, no," I said. "You've got it wrong. It's the other way around. I've found my mind, and I don't like anything about it."

They took action, filing reports and discussing my needs. At first, they put me on suicide watch, locking me in a medical isolation cell, naked except for a mat with a hole in it through which I stuck my head.

"I don't want to die," I told the nurses. "I'm not nuts."

It took them a week or two, but the nurses soon believed the first part of my argument, although they doubled down against the last. "He needs psych meds," I heard one urge the doctor.

Doc slurred his words in agreement, and I thought I heard him prescribe me a daily dose of rum and Coke.

"Remeron," the night nurse said when she brought me the first green and white capsule the size of a baby's pinky. "It's a mild drug to treat your mental health."

I declined it, argued, swore I wasn't crazy, but the more I said it, the more she disbelieved me. She called for the C.O. on duty, and the C.O. threatened to write me up for refusing an order, which wouldn't have mattered to me if I had been insane, but because I wasn't, it made perfect sense. So, I needed to pretend. I swallowed the pill and cooperated as the C.O. searched me to make sure I hadn't palmed it or hidden it under my tongue. Satisfied, he left. The nurse followed, saying just before she closed the cell door, "This won't fix you, but it'll help."

A few minutes passed, then panic overtook me. I couldn't breathe. I shook. I sweated. I was terrified that, with my clear thoughts, I'd experience this medication the way one might a medieval torture chamber: the feel of fingernails ripped out one by one, perhaps, or a hot iron pressed against my shin. I tried to stand so that I could pace my cell in anxious anticipation, but my legs denied me, my shoulders grew heavy, and I sensed the touch of the chaplain's god as I lay back down. I saw shadow people dancing around me like photonegatives of flames. I heard a peaceful hum inside my head. "Thank you," I said, not sure to whom. This was what I had wanted all along.

Real Cowboys Don't Accessorize

Marty Walsh

Part myth, part movie, part American
icon—real cowboys don't accessorize
like rodeo dudes and rodeo stars do.
Like the bull rider in black chaps
and black ten-gallon hat big as a
howdah on an elephant's back
pulling on rhinestone-studded
black leather gloves and mounting
a black bull in the chute then raising
his glitzy free hand over his head,
digging in his knees, goading
the behemoth red-eyed berserker
he's seated on, twisting the braided
rope looped around its massive
girth with his right hand til it pinches—
enrages—risking his neck for 8
seconds of fame in the dust-choked
arena. Later celebrating his cash prize
overall 2nd Place finish in riding,
roping and steer wrestling with
champagne. And an ice pack on
his purple-bruised left knee. Cowboy

coffee's reserved for ranch hands
like the one finishing off the dregs
of a pot made at noon and having
a smoke out on the porch while
canned chili's warming up on
the stove. The sun going down
and a distant buzzard circling lower
and lower between purple, dust-hazy
hills as he flicks his smoke over
the porch railing and heads inside,
bone weary from replacing fence posts
all day, thinking maybe he'll grab a beer
after supper and hit the sack early tonight.

Impending Heart Attack in the Doldrums on the Anniversary of Her Death

Romana Iorga

The neck, the shoulder, the arm.
　　The jawbone. You picture it
　　　　barren of flesh,
　　cracking a permanent grin.
Inflicting minuscule damage,
　　given its laughable girth.
　　　　Forget the one thousand
men. This mandible
of an ass can barely dispatch
　　one drunken fly.
　　　　Weak chin, your mother
　　said once. You agreed.
The brain names body parts,
　　assigning pain
　　　　where it must:
　　falsely enough to kill you.
You greet a ghost as a purveyor
　　of meaning. What's real is
　　　　irrelevant, unless
　　there's more to it: the veil

swept off—a flick of thought—to find
        some queasy truth within.
              Take love, for instance,
      or motherhood: both
cradle baby death sucking its thumb.
        Good morning, hypochondria!
             the figment rolls her eyes,
      forgetting she was so averse
to being helped, she died of it.
        What irony, to find yourself
            not nearly as different
      as you wished.
You've waited half your life to die,
        how do you know she didn't?
           Most people
      beg for solace with no one there.
What did you do to stave off
        the untimely 'fill in the blanks'?
           You watched her
      from afar: forlorn, derisive,
crippled by guilt.
        I've lived now twice
           as long as Christ—
      that's more than enough, she'd say
and all you did was nod.
        Not even forty then, how tired
           you were, how weak
      and how ashamed to want
exactly what she had.

You'd shared a body
　　　once, you'd earned
　　her laughter—why not
her illness?　　Ah, the bliss
　　　to pull apart the vise
　　　　　squeezing your ribs,
　　the foolish hunger
to hear her call you hers again.
　　Soon after, she went
　　　　and you stayed on.
　　You kept on staying.
Now, that it's closing in, the whopper
　　　meant to cart you far away
　　　　　from this god-awful
　　Land of Pointless Aches,
your mother's ghost flying ahead,
　　as she is wont to do,
　　　　what's left to say?
　　No *thank you, finally,*
no *where have you been?*
　　Only the recognition
　　　　that it's time, that once
　　it's over, no one will recall
your name. So few do hers.
　　We are but shadows
　　　　of lives fully unlived,
　　shadows of poems
ending none too soon.

The Closet

S.W. Campbell

The boy lays in his bed in the dark and listens to the animals in the closet. He can hear them talking to one another in low voices, the words inaudible, but the feeling permeating the darkened room. It is lonely in the closet. It is frightening to be alone. They don't understand why they have to be there. Why they must coldly roost on dusty shelves while others lay warm, encased under warm blankets pulled tight up to their chins. They are trapped, and they are unhappy. It is unfair, but there is nothing to be done.

Moonlight, etched by the shadowy branches of the locust trees, floats in through the windows, illuminating a world of indistinct gray shadows. Toy shelf, dresser, bunk bed, and bean bag chairs. All there, but not quite all the way. The boy sits silent and listens. He rolls towards the wall. Away from the view of the slightly ajar accordion of the closet door. Towards the lumps of Pound Puppy and Puppet who lay beside him.

Pound Puppy is the older of the two. Tan hide and stubby ears, sad plastic eyes glinting in the darkness, the sewn threads of a repaired blowout on his right hindquarters, and a neck wrung by the crook of an elbow until no more stuffing remains. They had all received Pound Puppies, once upon a time, but only this one still enjoyed the light of day, resting on his place next to the pillow. Puppet is the younger. An orange crochet body with a hole to allow in a hand, brown floppy ears, big bright red mouth, and two blue jewels for eyes. A gift from an old nurse to a little boy, then eight, who had lain in a hospital bed, saying nothing, watching the world, understanding too much, but feeling too worn out to care.

The boy clutches the pair to his chest. The ten dollar bill hidden inside Puppet crinkles beneath the pressure of his skinny arm. The boy is eleven. He is too old for such things. He knows this, but he can't seem to put them away. He is unable to banish them to the closet with the rest. They would be unhappy in the closet. It would not be right for them to be all alone. They are friends, confidantes, and companions. They stay quiet and they are always there. They never question and they never judge. From them he has nothing to hide. No thoughts are bad. No thoughts are good. They are just thoughts. Floating in an emptiness, bounced by echoes across the vastness of his mind. Free of the whispers of parents unaware that anyone is listening, not knowing how far one's name can carry in the dark.

When he was ten they had taken Blankie, soft white fabric which had been there from the start. The fringe ripped away and a small hole near one corner. Once held close against a frightened body, suddenly cleaved away and gone, taken while he was away at school. The parents had sat him down. They had explained how he was getting older. How it was time to give up such things. To them it had all seemed so reasonable. No question it was the right thing to do. The boy had thrown a fit. A tantrum that seemed to have no end. His brothers had watched from the periphery as his screams had shook the windows. He yelled until he could yell no more, took a rest, and then got back up to yell again. His parents did not break. The worst of the storm passed and the boy went to bed, his eyes full of tears. For a time he searched whenever he had a chance. All the closets, under his parents' bed, the brown chest in the living room, the attic, the crawlspace, the cellar amongst the Christmas lights. Nothing. The parents were too good at hiding. Blankie was gone, and that was that. Pound Puppy and Puppet took his place. A fight for another day.

On the lower bunk the boy's little brother farts in his sleep, rolls over, and farts again. The little brother is always farting in his sleep. A few times he has farted so bad that he has woken himself up, bursting into the world with a startled yelp of indignation that someone would dare to break his slumber. The little brother never hears the voices. The little brother is a good sleeper. He passes out the moment he's in bed, and he rises with the morning sun. He doesn't know about the world of the night, because he is never there to observe it. Not the rustle of the locust trees, the howl of the coyote, or the gurgle of the toilet. Not the mice skittering in the walls, the settling creak of the joists, or the shift of the logs in the wood stove. The sounds in the deep of night that nobody hears. The sounds that come out after even the whispered worries of the parents fall silent into guttural snores.

The boy does not sleep. His brain will not let him. It whirls in unending thoughts, stories, ideas, and worries. A mechanism of perpetual motion, never stopping until without warning it does, dropping him dead until jostling hands wake him to face the morning sun. He lays in his bed and waits for the sudden shift to the next day. He lays in his bed, quiet, listening to the world of the darkest part of night. They all have voices.

The toys argue amongst each other on the shelves, debating who will be the ones to be next played with. Sometimes the verbal turns to physical, and a favorite toy is shoved somewhere out of sight by other jealous playthings. In the drawers the clothing rustles. The shirts on top, looking forward to soon being worn, the shirts on the bottom, bemoaning the weight of their comfortable brethren, knowing they will never see the light of day. The boy is finicky about his clothing, and many shirts lie near the bottom, never worn. It is worst for those who were once near the top. Those who now have unsightly holes or stretched out necks. They remember what it had once been like. They remember a better world. But it is the animals in the closet that tug at his heartstrings. It is the animals for whom he feels. They do not want to be played with. They do not ask to be worn. They just want to feel close to something. To feel connected. To feel loved.

In the morning the bus will come and the boy will be taken to school. He will ride the forty-five minutes with his nose buried in his book. He will sit in class and listen. He will go out to recess to play. Sometimes with others, but more often than not alone. Each month he can feel the divide growing. Each year the chasm widens more. When he was younger he had just been one of many. Another set of bright eyes amongst the crowd. Now he doesn't belong. An outsider looking in. A voyeur on the world. When he was eight he was woken in the middle of the night and taken to the hospital. He stayed there for a week. When he returned he did so with a body made of sticks. Perhaps that was the reason why. In his head, the boy always imagines his body was once more like all the rest, less thin, less weak. No, it is probably just in his head. Things have always been this way. Even when he was small he had known it would just be a matter of time. There was something about him different. He was not like all the rest. He did not belong.

The boy shifts in his bed again. The ten dollar bill crinkles in Puppet's head. All the voices go silent for a moment, then start up once again. The boy's voice is still hoarse with screamed denials. An unending litany of refused acknowledgment. Life is not fair, but why should he be the one who must always take notice? The parents once said that they did not want to spoil him. They had spoiled him when he was little, and it had led to bad things. The boy has no memory of such a world. No thoughts to remind him of such a paradise. Did the parents say it often, or did they only say it once? Either way it is lodged deeply in his head. The idea that he is being punished for a world he can't remember. A world where he did not want. A world where things were fair. A world of which he was a part. A world where he was doing more than just looking in. A world where someone understood. Where others heard the voices. Where there were no worried whispers. Where nothing was alone. Gone. All gone without even a memory. Just a feeling that something is wrong. The sense that things will never get better, that they will only get worse. Why shouldn't he reach out and take whatever he needed? Who has the right to judge someone doomed to isolation?

The sad plastic eyes of Pound Puppy stare up at the boy. The blue jewel eyes of Puppet do not twinkle. With them the boy has no secrets. No defenses. They can see into his soul. He knows what they are thinking. Even the wanderer must have morals. Just because the chasm is widening, it doesn't mean he should try to escalate its speed. No wrong can ever make the world feel right.

The boy rises up and the voices cease. The boy pulls the ten dollar bill from Puppet's head and holds it tightly in his hand. He slips down the bunk bed ladder, doing his best to not make a sound. Little brother farts again, smacks his lips, and rolls over. Across the carpet. The bedroom door sticks, it must be yanked to be opened. Sit silent and wait to see if anyone heard. Even in the muted light, the boy can see the scars on the door's finish. Evidence of past battles with the world slipping by. The hallway is dark. No windows. Just the tiny orange flicker from the gap between the wood stove's gate in the distant living room. The dark shadow of the bathroom. The closed door of the room of older brother, and the slightly ajar door of the parents.

The boy creeps next to the ajar door and stops to listen. Heavy breathing. A high nasal snore. Familiar sounds. The constant background hum of the deep night. The boy pushes open the door. Moonlight splashes across the hall. Rustling in the bed. Freeze. Nothing. Stay low. Creep forward below their view. Stick up one bony hand. Feel the leather sitting on the cold lacquered wood. Bring it back down. Open it. Put in the ten dollar bill. Return the wallet to its place. Creep back out. Slowly. Put the door back into its original position. Sit and listen. Almost done. Crawl back into his room. Shut the door. Push it past where it sticks. Sit and listen.

The voices are going once again. The boy can hear the muffled sounds of the animals in the closet. Sad sounds. Quiet sounds. Hopeless sounds. The shadows of the locust trees shift with the rustle of the wind. The boy thinks about going back. He thinks about retrieving the ten dollar bill. He stays put. He listens. Poor bastards. Poor lonely bastards. Stuck. Alone. The boy stands and opens the metal folding closet door. The hinges squeal. The voices stop. The boy takes them in armloads and puts them up on the top bunk. Bee and pink elephant from the claw machine, big koala bear, little brother's pound puppy and stuffed cat, the clown puppet, sleepy alligator, older brother's ragged teddy bear, pink panther stiff with his wire bones, little velvet mouse, and all the rest. The boy climbs up and lays amongst them. Everything is quiet. Everything is good. He can feel their happiness. He can feel the joy coming off of them. Pound Puppy's plastic eyes don't seem so sad.

Philology

John P. Kristofco

My English words drift aimless
through the rooms inside my head,
sleep in gauzy beds
until I summon them
to edge
of where the world begins;
      though timid to return
to wind, rain,
the sunrise and the sunset of their birth,
fussy for their clarity,
the timbre of their names.

I shrug my abstract shoulders
at their angst,
considering Icelandic for a change,
rocky, rugged, nervy,
used to sleeping on the floor
and making earthy noise on steps,
scary, bold, almost unpronounceable,
a clatter
just like life.

Each Seed

Paulann Petersen

A smallest body sown
in the barrow. Bit of memory-bone.
The reliquary of color shape size.

A memento mori of mirror-life.
Archive for the ghosts of its every past.
Blueprint for each branching to follow.

From one seed a sum of life
spins backward. From that same one
all flows forth. Easy enough

to think of the seed's green flame
carrying lives to come.
Not so easy to feel—

in the almost nothingness
of its self in my palm—
the weight of enough deaths

to overgrow this earth.

Contingency

Jacob M. Appel

I had been asked to develop a contingency plan. This was my first as-signment. I was flattered to have been chosen. My boss said he wanted the plan on his desk by the end of the week. It was already Thursday. When he left, I realized that I did not know anything about the origi-nal plan for which we required a backup. By then, of course, it was too late to ask. I did not wish to embarrass myself on the first day. At my prior job—with the government—we did not have contingency plans. Often, we had no plan at all. We did have flextime and an excellent cafeteria that served up a top-notch Salisbury steak. The first weeks in my new position proved an adjustment. Getting to the office by nine o'clock had not been a picnic, and the rotisserie from the food carts across the avenue was hit-or-miss, so I always packed a cheese sand-wich. Once you know what emergency you are anticipating, it is easy to develop a plan B.

But with my assignment, I did *not* know what emergency re-quired anticipation. Nor what existing plan such a crisis threatened. Our firm manufactured thousands of diverse products and provided sundry direct-to-consumer and business-to-business services across six continents. It seems unlikely that any threat might endanger *all* the conglomerate's endeavors. And would they really trust addressing this menace to a new hire with a night school MBA? But I had been allotted a task, so I did my utmost to tackle it. I spent the next three hours in my cubicle cataloguing existential dangers to the firm's ongoing operations: an impact event from a comet or meteor; nuclear winter; simultaneous currency collapses in North American, Europe and Asia. None of these events seemed to lend themselves to contingency management so much as they did a planetary eulogy or requiem. But it was the company dime, not mine, so I tried to develop initiatives both concrete and outside-the-box. I also made a list of questions, because supervisors tend to like lists of questions. I asked: "Who owned the rights to after-the-comet.com? What did the profit margins look like in iodine and Geiger counters?"

When my list was complete, I broke out my cheese sandwich. Then I decided to discuss the matter with Snipe. He was in a different division of our department, reporting to a parallel chain of command, but he'd been with the firm for more than two decades, so he knew what was what. I had heard him advising Hawkins, the other recent hire, regarding the rotisserie.

Snipe wore suspenders and stashed a grocer's pencil above his left ear. He smelled like the office. Even on the street, he smelled like the office. Or maybe the office smelled like Snipe. Who could conclusively say?

I told him I'd been assigned a contingency plan.

"A contingency plan," he replied. "Now that's a responsibility."

He scratched his pate. I hoped he might say more.

I asked him if he had any advice.

"Have you tried the rotisserie yet?" he inquired. "It's hit-or-miss. I recommend bringing a bag lunch for the worst days."

I thanked him. It was sound advice. When I returned to my cubicle, I found Hawkins waiting for me. He was young, and reed-thin, and sported a mustache-and-soul-patch-combo like Dizzy Gillespie. He'd previously worked in "The Industry," which I took to mean music or movies or something. To be honest, I did not care for Hawkins.

Hawkins had been looking at a framed photo of my wife. Holding it. Caressing it with his eyes. He was seated on the stacked cartons of copy paper beside my desk.

"Man, you got a minute?" asked Hawkins. "I need your help."

I waited for him to explain.

"I hear you're drawing up a contingency plan," he said.

I acknowledged this. It seemed word got around.

"Here's the thing, man. I've been asked to draw up a contingency plan for your contingency plan—a plan C, if you will. But that's hard to do if I don't know what your contingency plan looks like. You see my problem?"

So they had asked me to devise a plan B and had only asked him for the plan C. That was certainly a confidence booster.

"I hear you," I answered. "But I'm waiting on plan A."

Hawkins looked confused, maybe too much strain on his gray matter. "Plan A?"

"How can there be a plan B without a plan A?"

He wasn't sure if I was screwing with him. I smiled politely and thanked him for his time.

That night I discussed the problem with my wife. She's a marketing manager and she's practical. It is a second marriage for us both.

"Turn it around on them," she said. "Tell them they should solicit contingency plans from their employees. Better bottom-up than top-down. Maybe hold a contest. Contests are good for moral. Low cost. Give away surplus merchandise or gift cards."

I feared that sounded somewhat risky.

"If he doesn't like it," she said, "no loss. He'll just turn to Hawkins for plan C."

So a contest it was to be. Once I had a concept, filling in the details proved easy. The data regarding in-house contests is rather extensive: team-based round robins, sweepstakes, etc. When my boss arrived at four o'clock the following afternoon, I had my report ready. Hawkins watched from his cubicle. My palms sweated as my supervisor opened the manila folder containing my proposal.

That was when the alarms sounded. These were not the fire alarms they drilled us on. These were angry wails punctuated by arrhythmic clanging. Like cymbals playing during an air raid siren. Then the lights began to flash: white, red, ominous.

"I won't have time to read this," said my supervisor. "What's the plan?"

"We might have a contest," I shouted. "Solicit ideas from our workforce. Have we ever attempted a bottom-up approach to contingency planning?"

My supervisor's face turned the color of the warning lights.

"This is a crises," he screamed. "We need to put our contingency plan into place. Now!"

I did not have an opportunity to defend my approach further. He threw the file across the room and walked directly into Hawkins's cubicle. That was when the alarms went silent. "FALSE ALARM," announced the overhead speakers. "ALL CLEAR. FALSE ALARM."

They gave me six weeks of severance. I had only worked two weeks, so this seemed more than reasonable. But I was disappointed in losing the job. At first. I found another position within a month, a government post, different agency so it didn't affect my pension. They gave me credit for my time at the firm too. Called it expertise in contingency planning. That's what I do now. I'm the taxpayers' plan B. Since Washington is still developing plan A, my hours remain flexible. And the Salisbury steak is unparalleled here too. Must be a government thing. I tell people this was *my* contingency plan—which isn't exactly untrue—and you can't go wrong on Uncle Sam's payroll. It's good work if you can get it.

Poetry

Matthew J. Spireng

Two plastic gallon containers of water labeled *poetry*
have been placed on a table at the back of the room
with cookies and cups and a two-liter bottle

of ginger ale not labeled *poetry*, and I consider
the contents of the gallon containers, whether
the clear liquid that appears to be water might be

the essence of poems, whether it must be drunk
or the containers opened to allow the contents
to act. Imagine: the essence of poetry, bottled

and available to anyone with the strength to pull
the little plastic tab on the cap. Poetry: clear
and liquid and taking the shape of the container.

The Same Girl

Rachel Barton

The rhodie bore witness in silence; wads of blossoms cast-off like used tissues littered underfoot. The five o'clock sun of mid-March lent light but little warmth to the evening air. The same girl sat at the curb huddled into her cell phone, bunched up in her hoody and hunched over. She didn't perch in front of her own home but a quarter of a lawn away where the laurel provided a screen; she didn't want her own "peeps" to observe her. All of her body language spoke of a desire to transcend the laws of space and time, to slip seamlessly into the airwaves where her beloved's disembodied voice crooned to her night after night. Instead, her buttocks complained to her of the cold seeping through the cement; neighborhood children buzzed by on roller blades making it hard to hear; the curbs began to fill with the cars of residents returning home at the end of the day. No wall, not even a cigarette could shield her from the realities of her suburban existence. The hedge of laurel seemed to commiserate.

She hung up the phone and rubbed her cigarette butt into the round of the curb before stowing it in her pocket. A lone cat, black with white socks, peered out from under the parked car next to her, as if to ask her for something, inquiring in a meowing kind of voice if she was the one who liked to rub her belly or scratch behind her ears; if so, she was agreeable. Yes, she was the same girl who rubbed this cat's belly every night after her phone call back east; she commenced to smooth the fur of her opportunistic friend. She wasn't ready to go inside and crack the books just yet and she certainly didn't want to share anything of her personal life with her doltish roommates.

The cat rested her paws on the hands of her human-of-the-moment, claws politely sheathed so that the relaxed weight of her footpads could impress upon her admirer the degree of her surrender, however momentary. She prolonged this coveted attention by commencing to purr whenever the human began to shift as if to stand, but, finally, the girl did stand and stretched like a cat herself, long arms reaching up and behind her head, back arching slightly, arms opening to either side of her chest, and then dropping to her sides. Though it was more of the *mountain satsana* than the *Cat/Cow*, she could feel the cat's approval of her display. She had internalized Hittleman's Hatha Yoga over the last seven years, stretching herself through adolescence to womanhood with grace and strength.

Inside the door, she shed her hoody, slipped off her shoes, and with the quiet of cat feet removed herself to the kitchen to make a cup of tea. She swatted her own cold butt several times to increase the circulation before the kettle began to whistle. She took her time rinsing her favorite mug in warm tap water, filling the tea infuser with loose-leaf Darjeeling, and then steeping the tea the requisite four minutes; the ritual of tea, like her yoga practice, was a tool for centering. She added a teaspoon of honey and headed down the hall to her bedroom, mug in hand. Perhaps the Lilliputians would defeat Gulliver after all and she could kick Jonathan Swift to the back of the cupboard until the next millennium; she was irked with him for being obtuse and self-involved—no, wait, that was the boyfriend. *Oh, what the hey; they were both annoying.*

"There she is again, Dad. Why do you suppose she is always out there?" Jack let the sheers drop and turned to his dad who was reclining before the evening news. No response. His dad had his hearing aids hooked up to the television so he didn't hear anything else. Jack peered into the narrow ellipse of an opening between sheers and studied his subject again. He wondered if her butt wasn't getting cold, if she missed her family, if she smoked when she was at home. He figured she had come from back east because she made her calls in broad daylight which would allow for the difference in time.

He had witnessed clusters of students move in and out of that house over the last few years, with the same tired particle-board desks, the IKEA shelving, and the giant speakers and sound systems. He hadn't seen the arrival of the GameCubes or PlayStations of the present occupants, personally, but he suspected they were there from the screen auras he observed at odd hours throughout the night. Last count, three students now lived in the house. The two guys worked regular jobs; Safeway and Domino's uniforms identified their employers. He wasn't sure about the girl.

He imagined her life in a story he wrote for his high school creative writing class, imagined that she was a brilliant scientist trapped in a parallel universe who couldn't get back to what she regarded as real. Instead of engaging in the world around her, she pined for what she had left behind. This created a hole in her "field"—her life force was leaking into the past, sucked into a wormhole created by her emotions. The story did not have a happy ending, though he reworked it several times. He kept watching her to monitor any shifts in behavior so that he could change the outcome, but, so far, nothing new. There was still time for an epiphany of some kind; he had until the end of the semester to turn in his final draft. He went to the fridge for a soda and

headed up to his room to finish his homework—math and Spanish—
he would be done before Mom called him to dinner.

Violet, the owner of the sky blue Nissan *Leaf*, sighed as she approached
her house; the same girl was perched on the curb and glued to her
phone as Violet had observed her every evening since the term had
begun. She pulled carefully into her driveway and parked. The girl had
hung up her phone but was still sitting in the same position. What was
it about this patch of cement that attracted her so consistently? Violet
looped her purse over her shoulder and opened her car door, leaned
in to gather the bag of groceries, and stood up just in time to see the
first rays of sunset flinging fingers of golden light into the vault of blue
heaven; to her, this valley was Eden. She nodded to the girl and then to
her screen of laurels in appreciation, as she stepped around the wilted
blossoms of the rhodie at the edge of her drive, and walked to her door.
The density of laurel leaves brought her right back to her own quiet
garden where the peonies would lay down their heavy blossoms all the
way to the ground, and the lavender, open into aromatic splashes of
blue-violet whether she weeded or not. She stewarded as best she could
but the garden was really in charge of itself.

Violet shifted the grocery bag up her hip and deftly unlocked her
door. As she unpacked her provisions of baguette, fresh pasta, pesto,
and salad greens, she wondered what the girl ate in the house next
door. She knew too well that a student might squeak by on a diet of
Ramen noodles. She resolved to invite her in one evening for a bite of
supper to learn more about her. Violet put on a pot of water for the pasta and chopped the scallions and cilantro to add to the greens for the
salad. Then she filled the cat's water bowl and added some tuna to her
dry food; Boots was her treasure—she spared no expense. Now where

was that cat? She called out the kitchen window, "Here, kitty-kitty, come get your supper!" Boots bounded to the sill from the back porch and scooted through the opening with a practiced slither, then sure-footed across the sinks to the floor. She acknowledged her owner with a rub of her body against a pant leg before diving into her food. Violet smiled, totally gratified, and continued with her dinner preparations.

The girl pulled her bike into her driveway and walked through the house, dislodging her backpack from her shoulders with a clunk, and opening the garage door to stow her bike and helmet, the ping of a basketball bouncing off cement in the background. She stood with her hand on the button to the garage door as she watched the boy across the street shoot baskets. There was something about him that seemed inviting to her, something idyllic about playing basketball in the street before dark. She paused for a minute longer and then he turned to her.

"Come on over!" was all he said.

She felt her heart thumping a little harder in her chest, adrenaline rising. The cell phone in her pocket weighed heavy with the obligation she put upon herself to call her boyfriend every evening. What if she didn't? She set the phone on the washing machine just inside the door and jogged across the street. She couldn't explain why she felt so elated. Whatever the cause, she was glad to be moving in her body, to be in the moment. The maple tree in the front yard fluttered its fresh green leaves, pointy little flags not fully shapened, as the wind blew her hair across her face. She twisted and tucked the bulk of it into the back of her shirt and stuck out her hand.

"I'm Lucy."

"Call me Jack." He was surprised she had responded and was quick to up his game for her benefit. He landed a net ball with a clean swish and bounced the rebound over to her. She looked lean and limber to him, but he didn't know what skills she had or what kind of stamina. He played a moderately aggressive defense which she successfully dodged, lofting the ball high into a graceful lay-up. Not bad, he thought. He pushed himself a little harder; she continued to match him until they were tied, eight to eight.

"Nice game. I take it you played hoops in high school?" Jack was still catching his breath but he didn't want her to slip away yet. She was still a mystery to him.

"I played a lot of street ball with my brothers back in Tarentum. That's in Pennsylvania if you want to know. We live on one of the few level streets in town; most of them in our neighborhood head down to the river, but we're on one of the cross streets. We used to plant our basketball hoop at the end of the drive and play until the fireflies came out and Mom called us to dinner." Lucy paused to marvel at how easily she could share her story with this boy. "Both my brothers are in Iraq right now." She smiled at Jack and bounced the ball to him before she headed back across the street. "Tough as nails. I know they'll be OK," she said, to herself as much as to Jack. She didn't have to share everything.

"Maybe tomorrow?" Jack hollered. He had more questions than ever.

"Maybe..." her voice trailed off as the garage door made its slow descent.

Jack made his way to the house, puzzling over the new information. She had finally changed her behavior; she wasn't on the phone. She had a name, she had brothers, and boy, could she play ball! He wondered what it meant that she wasn't on the phone. Had she had a falling out with the boyfriend? If so, she didn't seem sad about it. He'd have to think about this some more, or, better yet, talk to her some more real soon.

The days were getting longer—more time to play hoops. With his buddy, Tony, out of town until after Spring Break, Jack was especially happy to have made a new friend courtside. None of the girls he knew at school would be caught dead playing ball with a boy. They were more engrossed in sophomoric behaviors like giggling and flirting from the safety of their cliques. Well, he was a sophomore, too, but that stuff just seemed too silly. He listened to a couple girls who read their stories aloud in class, and nearly made him cry, they were so good. One day, maybe... His week out of school was looking less like a black hole and more like a good time. Jack smiled to himself as he sloughed off his size tens inside the door. He stuffed the ball into the hall closet and bounced into the kitchen.

"What's for dinner? I'm starved!"

Violet sat down at her kitchen table the first week in April and composed her invitation:

To the girl on the curb, from your neighbor at 2230; I would be delighted if you would join me for supper on Friday evening, just after dark—I'll keep the porch light on.

—Yours, Violet Dupre and Boots (the cat!)

She slipped the note into a lavender envelope, licked it shut, and walked it around the laurels to the house with the maple tree. She snugged the note into the door jamb and returned home where she could consider the menu; she hadn't had a guest for some time. Should she offer wine? Yes, she would serve wine as she was drinking it anyway. And she could make a big green salad, roast some redskin potatoes, and find a nice piece of fish for the grill—simple but hearty;

she wanted to nourish that skinny little thing. Lately, she had noticed that the girl was not always on the curb. She had moved across the street to the basketball hoop some evenings, no longer tethered to her phone. That was a good sign, she thought. Her dahlia starts at the bay window nodded to her in agreement. They were nearly ready to be transplanted to the flower bed in the back. She would harden them off and plant them on the weekend.

Spring seemed a little late this year what with the quick freeze last week and more than the usual amount of wind. It left her feeling there was a storm around the corner, though, so far, only blustering. She could see a bit of fresh snow on Mary's Peak as she drove to work in the mornings, but that was a phantom dusting that couldn't last, could it? Violet pulled her sweater closed and got up to brew some tea, which upset the cat from her lap for which she fired a look of indignation towards Violet and retreated to the couch in the next room. Violet sighed. She had been soothing ruffled feathers all day, every day; as that was her job at Hospital Admissions. Well, she could soothe the cat, too. It had a way of coming right back to her; Boots was that kind of animal. Violet brewed her tea in silence.

"Dad, do we know anybody in Iraq?" Jack sat down to baked mac'n cheese and a big green salad; his mom knew his favorites. Since his sister had left for college, his mom had been more solicitous, as if she were aware of how soon he, too, would be out of the house. Two years seemed like a long time to him, hundreds and hundreds of math problems from now, but he wasn't about to point this out to her and discourage the extra attention. He looked up from his plate to see if his dad would answer.

"That's an interesting question, Jack. Yes, we know someone. Bill's son, Jason, shipped out in January. And Sherri, do you remember her? She was the girl at the front desk last summer—she left in June and should be back before the summer is over. I think she signed up with the Guard. What makes you ask?"

Jack could hear the worry in his dad's voice. "Dad, it's not about me; it's the girl next door, the one who plays ball. She's got two brothers over there. I just wondered what it was like, what they were going through." He didn't want to ask straight out, *would they ever come back*, but that's what he was wondering. His dad's face clouded over like the low-ceilinged skies of the past week; he turned again to Jack as if to assess his maturity, as if to ask if he had prepared him for the world of men.

Jack waited patiently, hoping to come out on the right side of the question. He thought back to their discussions about *The Things They Carried*, last month's reading for his AP Lit class. His dad had read the book with him, sharing fragments of his own war experiences which tended to spring upon him, and his family by association, in one exploding grenade after another if he wasn't mindful. Jack had understood this volatility intuitively; he had no romantic ideas about war.

"It's not southeast Asia, Jack, so I can only guess from some of the serious news reporting that we see occasionally on TV." Jack listened to his dad summarize the politics and climate surrounding the war in Iraq. Soaring temperatures, body armor or the lack of it, friendly fire, scrambled intelligence—the list of hazards made the deepest impression; the politics fell by the wayside. He could only conclude that the odds were not favorable for the return of Lucy's brothers, at least not without injury. What had been a casual rapport with a girl on a curb had become something deeper, tinged with compassion and the anticipation of loss. Jack consumed his second plate of mac'n cheese thoughtfully; he lived a charmed life. What responsibility comes with that, he wondered?

A freak hailstorm pelted the windows for thirty seconds and then stopped. The patio was carpeted in minute pellets of ice like rock salt. Jack looked up at the sky to ask, *What? What are you trying to tell me?* But no answer was forthcoming.

Violet arranged the freshly-cut lilac blossoms in a vase and put them on the table. She was grilling burgers tonight at Lucy's request. Lucy would bring the potato salad and apple crisp—flavors from home. They had shared three Fridays in April; this would be the fourth. Violet mulled over their conversations as she brewed the ice tea and chopped fresh veggies in lieu of a salad; they were going to eat in the garden if it was warm enough. She seasoned the patties of ground beef and preheated the grill.

So far, she knew that Lucy was twenty-two years old, in her third year of college as an English major, and far from her home in Pennsylvania. She had two brothers, Jason and Robert, both in Iraq, and her parents ran a small print shop in Pittsburgh that specialized in engraved wedding invitations. Her mother wrote to her once a week and her brothers had written twice since they shipped out in November.

The boyfriend, Ron, was in school, at Dartmouth, and never wrote—he preferred the telephone. They were going through a cool spell right now as the long-distance relationship was wearing on both of them. Violet thought he was a self-centered jerk who didn't deserve Lucy, but she kept this to herself. She was more interested in the brothers as Lucy's face grew softer when she spoke of them.

"Violet? Are you home? May I come in?" Lucy stepped into the little hallway that melded into living room, hung her hoody on the hook behind the door, and carted her foodstuffs to the kitchen just in time to catch Violet coming in the back door with a sprig of fresh mint.

"Hello Lucy! Welcome once again! Just put the crisp on the counter—the tile can take the heat—and you can pop the potato salad in the fridge until we're ready to sit." Violet had grown up with a healthy paranoia about mayonnaise and picnic food. She bruised the mint in two tall glasses of ice, and then poured the strong tea to the brim. "Shall we sit in the garden to see if it's warm enough?" She motioned to the sliding door which Lucy opened. They sat under the pergola in camp chairs, nursing the tumblers of sweetened tea, as the spring tulips nodded off for the evening and the tree toads took up a chorus. When Violet grilled the burgers, they moved inside to the kitchen table; they were too hungry to dicker with stink bugs or gnats and it had grown cooler into evening than was seemly for an outdoor picnic.

Violet wrapped her shoulders in the fleece shawl from the back of the kitchen chair and grabbed another from the couch for Lucy. *In the northwest, it's all about layers*, she thought. Then she spread the felt-backed vinyl tablecloth and set the table with a set of the brightly-colored Melmac of her childhood which she had found at the Goodwill a couple years back; they could pretend they were outdoors. The heady lilac spoke to them in perfumed puffs as the conversation wandered down the back roads of their well-lived lives.

Jack was startled from the curf of incandescence that illuminated his desktop. He looked up from his probability equation—something about fertilizers and predicted yields—and listened intently. He didn't hear so much as sense that someone was in trouble. From his upstairs window, he scanned the patches of illuminated street below, the driveways, the sidewalks…there she was, weeping into the phone, holding her abdomen with her free arm as if the pain were physically crushing her from the inside out. It wasn't the boyfriend; they were taking a month off. Suddenly Jack knew. He leapt from his chair, jumped into his sneakers, and hollered to his mom.

"Mom? Where's that phone number for the lady across the street, Mrs. Dupre? This is important, Mom." He was sliding down the banister and jumping off into the kitchen hallway when she met him with the piece of paper from the side of the fridge. "Thanks. I love you, Mom." He hugged her quickly and dialed the number. When she answered, he just said, "Something's happened. She's on the curb." His voice cracked slightly. Then he was out the door.

His mother and father watched in silence from the front window, arms around each other. Violet brought a blanket from the house and put it over Lucy's shoulders. The cat slithered under the tent of her bent knees. Violet and Jack sat very close to the girl as if to keep her from shaking. Then all three of them were weeping together. Chinaberry blossoms snowed pale pink petals at their feet. The rhodie nodded with a deep green gravity, its blossoms already spent.

You in Mind

Cecil Morris

When I think of you now, these long years after,
I think first of your brain, the gray-pink convolutions
of the cerebrum billowing over cerebellum and brain stem,
the whole thing (being doing knowing) floating in skull and meninges
and constantly replenishing fluid like the protective
redundancies NASA designs. I think of you blooming
(like the cerebrum) from cells and processes, from aggregations
of dendrites and axons and synaptic structures
tangled in electrochemical embraces
that confabulate you—really the you of you—
the you I see when I close my eyes
and meet you in the darkest dark of disembodied self
or when you rescue me on darkling plains of doubt, disgust,
despair—the you whose touch touches deeper than skin or bone
or soft tissue and resonates (unmeasured unmitigated)
and tunes the me of me. When I think of you now,
this twilight that stretches obliquely on,
I think of action potential, of ionization
and neurotransmitters, of impulses jumping
synaptic voids and racing through me and back to you.

When I think of you now, I think of us,
of the curving universe folding on itself, of infinite
intricate lacework overlapping, of interleaving
webs interweaving nets of gold to airy thinness beat
and wove and linked and making the platonic us,
an integrated multicircuit of matched capacitance.

SWAK

Love letters always end up
in museums, the curious are
more persistent than lovers.
       —Adam Zagajewski, "Ode to Plurality"

Susannah B. Mintz

It was because my friend Richard died that I began thinking about the mail, about the fact that I would no longer receive envelopes from 19th Street in Seattle, with my name drawled across the front in purple ink, my middle initial carefully recorded, the sevens of my then-zip code inconsistently crossed in the European style. The last letter from that address, postmarked 2 Sep. 1993, was typed on soft beige paper—like a first grader's copy-book—with a pencil drawing on the back entitled "Laughter," and carelessly folded to fit the envelope. It was because my friend died that that letter, and all the others I had from him, suddenly contained mysterious significance, that they were full of portentous weight. I searched the letters for hints he knew he was becoming ill, wishing he had supplied me with a vocabulary for understanding his loss. I noticed that the last envelope was addressed in black, not purple, that the handwriting seemed hysterical, uncontrolled, almost illegible. I didn't want to make too much of this, but they were unignorable details. I found myself thinking in clichés: *These letters are all I have of him*, or *This is the last letter he wrote to me before he died.* I read and re-read the letters just to hear his voice again, his musings. They were sacred relics. But even before he died, in a tangible way, they had replaced him.

Richard's letters were not the only ones I kept. In a long rectangular box, covered in quilted blue silk, at the back of my closet, and in small ratty gift bags, in baskets and in manila folders stuffed in a beat-up file cabinet—hundreds of notes and letters, some going all the way back to seventh grade. Who, of a certain age, does not have some tucked away, still (even in a digital age), from that certain person, from that watershed year? Emissaries and ambassadors to and from other lives. All the lives we've ever inhabited, the selves we might have lost were it not for the stated record of what we once cared to document and save. From high school: my best friend warning that if I didn't choose between two boys I would lose them both. From college: a letter from the dean informing me of academic probation, for a prank I still recall every moment of enjoying.

When Richard moved to Seattle from Manhattan, where we'd both gotten MFA's in poetry at Columbia, his letters took his place in the life I continued on without his daily presence. I believe he would have written to me in his slanted hand even if we were more accustomed then to email. We spoke by phone no more than two or three times in the two years between his move and his death. But we wrote to each other regularly, and those letters took on an ease and familiarity, like weekly lunches; they encapsulated presentations of ourselves, a kind of brief performance, a one-act play of thought and emotion. We both had an instinctive distrust of telephones, of the sort of contact a phone call represents: immediate, live, unrehearsed. The closeness of speech and voice without the benefit of registering facial expression filled us with an unnamable dread that even our loneliness, how much we missed our friendship, did not override. But letters we could carefully construct, with the luxury of time to compose words precisely. We could compose ourselves, as well, in the ecstatic freedom of the page, in a passion for language. Richard was a better letter-writer than a poet; he could expose and protect himself simultaneously in letters in a way that allowed him to philosophize and contemplate freely. His letters were never mundane in detail, but the mundane anguish—*it has come to my attention that this beautiful woman on a bicycle rode by my house without stopping, without waving, without blowing me a kiss*—was so immense, so graceful, in his writing of it.

I kept Richard's letters in part because I liked the feel of them, small, neat stacks of legal envelopes I put in chronological order. I liked their weight and texture; they reminded me of Richard himself, of his body—not tall, rectangular somehow, compact from 25 years of daily running (which he did to keep himself from daily drinking). After his death, that texture, that weight, seemed grounding, seemed comfortably tangible, something *present*, in all the unbounded sorrowfulness of loss. Richard was not a particularly orderly person but his letters felt that way, exactly sized, the only roughness the ragged tear I made myself, opening them.

I asked Richard once if he had ever had a sensation of fear so intense, so physical, it was like a delirious spinning, a fear that whatever fragile cord attaching us to this world, to each other, might be snapped, and we would suddenly be out of control, lost to ourselves, to friends, to sanity. His answer was unexpected and blunt, but quintessential, and I will always remember it. He said, "You mean, like you're gonna croak?" I had not considered death until that moment, so focused was I on present, situational anxiety. I knew people who thought about death every single day of their lives, and I realized then that

Richard must have been one of them. I knew he was excessively aware of his age; so much about his life bespoke a near-desperate effort to ward off growing old—younger friends, exercise, a kind of deliberate immaturity about his finances. And a panic about how much there was left that he wanted to accomplish. Writing—poetry, letters—was his way of *remaining*. Every word of those letters was a part of him, flaked off onto the page. His remains. I noticed that he began to write more voluminously towards the end, as if he were trying to reconstitute himself there, in language, in folded pieces of paper sent around the country to his friends, his keepers.

In a letter close to the start of his illness, he wrote to me of his plans for future writing projects: he was working on a new manuscript of poems, and a play based on a poem he'd written called "Buffalo, Wyoming: The Day I Shot My Car." I remember that poem; it did not quite live up to the promise of the title. But in a way, Richard did. He was full of landscape, light and spaces, treks by car across swathes of country punctuated by towns with famous names. Buffalo. Jackson Hole. Namur, Brussels. Saigon. And a wry humor, an eye for the absurd contiguities of experience, for the poetic impulse in each of us that turns minor events into personal myths, that moves us to remember and tell, to embellish but also to reveal; to be brutal, honest. It is fitting that Richard's body was cremated, that his ashes were scattered over Puget Sound, and he became part of the scenery he adored.

In the days of letters, I used to wait nervously for the mail to come. Another day, another possible connection, some view of a faraway place, some confirmation of my existence through a friend's words. I'd hold off going to check the box as long as I could, maybe even skip a day, letting excitement coil through me. *Right now a letter could be waiting.* That was my daily ritual: anticipate, attenuate. As a teen (before bills, before an inbox), I'd fly to the front door at the thrum of the mail truck down our hill, then the screak of the mailbox, then the mail dumped in. Oh, that sickening thrill—would my fingers catch the thick edge, the ivory or pale blue, the youthful script, of an envelope for me? Even the disappointment was part of the rhythm of the day. Another afternoon, another reason to look forward to tomorrow. I long believed that the problem with Sundays—that feeling of malaise, that blank ennui—had something to do with the absence of mail, nothing to split the day apart. No fluctuation or tonal modulation, no orderly sense of *before the mail, after the mail.*

I remember, once, a dissatisfying trip to the mailbox: two bills for my parents, supermarket circulars, a free rag offering night classes for singles, a letter from my grandmother. And now a mouthful of guilt, because I received her letters like junk mail, not nearly special or interesting enough. Of course I didn't know how precious that letter would seem only months later—and would now, if I had kept more of them in all those boxes and bags—when they had become "all I had of her." When she died, it was less her voice over the phone, or the possibility of seeing her, or even the fact of her, that I was aware of missing, than the presence of her frequent letters—the familiarity of her handwriting, the cream-colored envelopes recognizable at a glance; the way she always included her full name with the return address, the movement of script across 20-lb. bond. She always addressed me in letters as *Darling.*

My grandmother's ashes rattled in a silver box. Chunky bits of bone in a box that had become her body. I held that box, but no longer remember if I opened it to look, ever voyeuristic, but also afraid, as if an eye might open out of the volcanic residue, the outline of a finger still visible in the crags of ash. My father took my grandmother, alone to the ocean, and threw her to sea.

Does Puget Sound meet the Pacific?

This is what letters remind us: that our lives are a perpetual condition of absence. Letters may accuse: *you were not there, I needed you.* Or they head such reproaches off at the pass. My mother has written to me more consistently than anyone else in my life. I've saved every single thing she has ever sent, from letters to cards to brief Post-it notes stuck to clippings and cartoons, the texture of all this correspondence reminding me of how long I have been *away*, and how my mother, eager for me to explore, has made sure I know how to return. Letters are what remain; this is why we feel compelled to store them, to hoard them (even, against all awareness of resources, to print the email in which something is *said*). A man I once knew threw all my letters to him into the Missouri River, and because the Missouri does end up in the Pacific, he thought he was returning them to me—I lived in California then—making a gesture of love. *I can't hold onto you anymore,* he wanted to say, *so I am returning you to you.*

Freud claimed that the process of mourning involves an almost obsessive re-experiencing of one's memories of the lost, loved person. He called it "hyper-cathecting." During the first week after I found out that Richard had died, I felt myself almost willfully having to bring up thoughts of him, to focus on my grief, so great was the pressure to have it subside, to subdue it, so that I could return to my "life." Then, as later, his letters were what I went to for a sense of him, the voice there no different than when he was alive, since our friendship had unfolded in letters for over two years.

There was time in my life when I preferred to carry on a love affair in letters—opening letters like undressing, folding and sealing them like rituals of touch. Written in a time that is already past by the moment they become immediate again in the hands of the other. In the first year of being separated from my husband, when he was back home in Canada for a time, I suggested we might carry out an entirely epistolary relationship punctuated by the occasional clandestine interlude in Niagara Falls. I imagined we might heal ourselves that way; free of the encumbrance of how our bodies had harmed us—the uncomprehending look, the turned back, the empty side of the bed when someone has failed to come home on time—the cool composition of language would save us. In fact we conducted much of the early despair of separation through text messages, which I occasionally captured as screen shots and then emailed to myself and then printed. Each of these technologies moved me further away from the emotional chaos of conversation with him, but also solidified a part of him—the way he could render our mutual bafflement in the pith of that tiny screen, all our sadness and remorse compressed there in crystalline terms—and let me carry something of that understanding close to my breaking heart.

A few years ago, in a fit of cleanliness, I unburdened my closets of several garbage-bags-full of mail. Years of birthday and holiday cards, going-away notes from friends at jobs I quit, reams of email printed and sorted and shoved into plastic bins and one overflowing cedar chest. Into a green bag went Richard's letters, with their spidery purple ink, their wit and their pathos, their trust in being received and held. I convinced myself that Richard would survive in my memory beyond his letters just as they had lasted beyond him, and perhaps I felt, as I often have, that some version of myself rising up from Richard's address to me had become irrelevant, or embarrassing, or intolerably sad because no longer true, or too true to bear rereading.

It did not take long, of course, for me to regret that rash act. Bereft of his timbre and vernacular, with no access to his habits of mind, I can only commemorate the idea of what had been so carefully wrought, can only remind myself of all those missives that once got sealed, I'm sure of it, with a kiss.

Look

James B. Nicola

You left to have a look within yourself, you said, without
me getting in the way. I took you at your word. I doubt
you can imagine how it felt, to be alone again.
I hoped that you would have a good look and be back. But *When?*,
I asked myself, over and over, learning to survive
without the least idea of why you'd left, or I'm alive,
other than that when you'd told me I never looked within,
just outward—that that's who I'd always be, and always been—

you must have been correct. And that "the gap between us" was
too deep, too wide, to ever be traversed, because—. Because.
And last night, on the avenue, while seeing you was sweet,
I don't think that it crossed my mind, when I crossed the street,
that you would either have to cross as well, or have to shout
my name to bridge the distance. I was just—looking out.

Contributors

Chris Anderson is a recently retired professor at Oregon State University, a Catholic deacon, and author of a number of books, poetry and prose, most recently a book of poems, *You Never Know*, published by Stephen F. Austin State University Press.

Jacob M. Appel is the author of three literary novels including *Millard Salter's Last Day* (Simon & Schuster/Gallery, 2017), eight short story collections, an essay collection, a cozy mystery, a thriller, and a volume of poems. He currently teaches at the Mount Sinai School of Medicine in New York City.

Rachel Arteaga works in higher education, with a focus on supporting the humanities. She completed the PhD in English at the University of Washington in 2016. She lives with her family in Seattle.

Bruce Barrow writes, bikes, and makes films in Portland, Oregon.

Rachel Barton is a poet, writing coach, and editor. She is a member of the Calyx Editorial Collective, reads for *Cloudbank*, and edits her own *Willawaw Journal*. Find her poems in *Oregon English Journal*, *Hubbub*, *Whale Road Review*, *Mom Egg Review*, and elsewhere. Her stories have appeared in *BeZine*, *Kindred Journal*, and *Blue Cubicle Press*. Her chapbook, *Out of the Woods*, was released in 2017. *Happiness Comes* was released from Dancing Girl Press in 2018.

Nathan Bas is a Clackamas Community College alumnus living in Oregon City, currently studying Creative Writing and English at Portland State University, soon to be published in *Polaris* and *CLR* as his first publications. He once had a passing whim to drop everything and live in a desert or forest, to write eccentric nonsense, but the likelihood of death, via thirst or cougar, was a deal-breaker. Now he spends moderately undue proportions of Christmas and birthday money on houseplants to create his own indoor jungle.

Ace Boggess is author of five books of poetry, most recently *Misadventure* (Cyberwit, 2020) and *I Have Lost the Art of Dreaming It So* (Unsolicited Press, 2018), as well as two novels, including *States of Mercy* (Alien Buddha Press, 2019). His writing appears in *Notre Dame Review*, *The Laurel Review*, *River Styx*, *Rhino*, *North Dakota Quarterly*, and other journals. He received a fellowship from the West Virginia Commission on the Arts and spent five years in a West Virginia prison. He lives in Charleston, West Virginia.

In October 2011, the poet's son, Josh, died by suicide. He was 43 years old. In the year that followed, **Andrea Campbell** attended weekly therapy and was encouraged to write a poem each month to process the loss and bring healing. That year was so rewarding that she went on to facilitate a support group for survivors of suicide loss until the present day. She has only published once before in a journal called the *Emerson Review*, while at Emerson College in 1960. It included poems by early Charles Bukowski, Denise Levertov, and William Stafford. She continued to write all her life but didn't try to publish again until this past year. She turned 80 years old in July 2019 and looks forward to poetry being central to the journey all the way to the end.

S.W. Campbell was born in Eastern Oregon. He currently resides in Portland where he works as an economist and lives with a house plant named Morton. He has had numerous short stories published in various literary reviews.

Geoff Cannard is a displaced Portlander who has been writing poems while following his academic wife through training overseas. Writing is his way to continue finding home even when he's far from it.

Marisa P. Clark is a queer writer from the South whose work has appeared in *Apalachee Review*, *Cream City Review*, *Potomac Review*, *Foglifter*, *Dunes Review*, *Rust + Moth*, *Whale Road Review*, and elsewhere, with work forthcoming in *Shenandoah*, *Nimrod*, *Epiphany*, *Burningword Literary Journal*, and *Evening Street Review*, among others. She was twice the winner of the Agnes Scott College Writers' Festival Prizes (in fiction, 1996; in nonfiction, 1997), and Best American Essays 2011 recognized her creative nonfiction among its Notable Essays. She reads fiction for New England Review and makes her home in New Mexico with three parrots and two dogs.

Thomas Cooper is a 19 year old writer of absurdist fiction from the United Kingdom. He takes inspiration from the work of Russian poet Daniil Kharms, for whom he believes demonstrated that it is often in the simplest of prose that the most meaning can be conveyed.

Brian Cronwall is a retired English faculty member from Kaua'i Community College in Hawai`i. His poems have been published in numerous journals and anthologies in Hawai`i, Guam, the Continental

United States, Australia, Japan, France, the United Kingdom, and Ireland, including recent publications in *Bamboo Ridge*, *Chiron Review*, *Hawai`i Pacific Review*, *Ekphrasis*, *Pinyon*, *Colere*, *The Santa Fe Literary Review*, *Grasslimb*, *The Carolina Quarterly*, *The Briar Cliff Review*, *Wild Violet*, *Avocet Review*, *Poetry Ireland Review*, *Common Ground Review*, and others.

Riley Danvers graduated in 2016 with her A.S. in English and in 2018 with her B.A. in English Literature and Writing. Riley was a student editor for two issues of the *Clackamas Literary Review* and was the Managing Editor of the online literary journal *M Review* for one year. Her fiction and nonfiction have been published in more than twenty online and printed literary journals and anthologies. Riley's poetry has been published in *Z Publishing House* and *Silkworm*.

Michelle DeLiso is accumulating a list of formers. She is a former reference librarian, magazine research editor, and writing instructor for children. She will soon be a former resident of New Jersey, but for now, that's where she lives with her husband and two sons.

Judith DeVilliers lives in Oregon. She writes weekly with friends, dabbles in watercolors, quilting, and baking bread. She does not consider herself a poet, though sometimes, not often, the words seem to organize themselves in what she considers a poem. She is planning on releasing her self-published novel, *Waking Lisa*, in 2020.

Erin Doyle is a social media specialist born and raised in Mahopac, New York. She was inspired to start writing poetry after reading *Life on Mars* by Tracy K. Smith and has since used the medium to reflect on attachment and heartbreak. An avid art lover, she also enjoys painting, drawing, and sewing.

Birch Dwyer is a writer, artist and poetry therapist. She offers workshops through Portland Women Writers and at Transition Projects, for women transitioning from homelessness. Her work has previously appeared in *Windfall*. She makes her home in Portland, Oregon, with her husband, son, and two dogs.

Jack Eikrem lives in Milwaukie Oregon. He is a graduate of Marylhurst University and an alumnus of Clackamas Community College. Jack's poetry has appeared in *Salal Review*; his fiction in *M Review*.

Sophie Estrada is a part time college student residing in Southern California. She has a passion for art, and loves to experiment with different mediums which include: drawing, digital art, sewing, and linocut printmaking. Sophie hopes to eventually find a career in which she can utilize her creative abilities.

Sharon Goldberg is a Seattle writer who was an advertising copywriter in a former life. Her work has appeared in *The Gettysburg Review*, *New Letters*, *The Louisville Review*, *Cold Mountain Review*, *River Teeth*, *Under the Sun*, *Chicago Quarterly Review*, *The Antigonish Review*, *The Dalhousie Review*, *The Raven Chronicles*, *The Manchester Review*, three fiction anthologies, and elsewhere. Sharon won second place in the On the Premises 2012 Humor Contest and Fiction Attic Press's 2013 Flash in the Attic Contest. She is an avid but cautious skier and enthusiastic world traveler.

John Grey is an Australian born short storywriter, poet, playwright, musician, and Providence, RI resident. He has been published in numerous magazines including *Weird Tales*, *Christian Science Monitor*, *Greensboro Poetry Review*, *Poem*, *Agni*, *Poet Lore*, and *Journal of the American Medical Association*, as well as the horror anthology *What Fears Become* and the science fiction anthology *Futuredaze*. He has had plays produced in Los Angeles and off-off Broadway in New York. He is the winner of Rhysling Award for short genre poetry in 1999.

Hilary Harper's writing has appeared in the *Connecticut River Review*, *Dime Show Review*, *Minerva Rising*, *Persimmon Tree*, and *Convergence*. She earned her MFA in creative writing from Queens University of Charlotte and lives in Kalamazoo, Michigan.

Joseph Harris is the author of *You're in the Wrong Place* (Wayne State University Press, Fall 2020). His stories have appeared in *Clackamas Literary Review*, *Midwest Review*, *Moon City Review*, *Great Lakes Review*, and have been nominated for the Pushcart Prize. He lives in Oak Park, MI.

Suzy Harris was born and raised in Indianapolis and has lived her adult life in Portland, OR. She is a retired attorney. Her poems have appeared in *Calyx*, *Clackamas Literary Review*, *Oyster River Pages*, *Rain*, *Third Wednesday*, *Willawaw Journal*, *Windfall*, and other journals and anthologies. She and her husband have two adult children who live in Portland, one dog, and a granddog.

Lisa Higgs' third chapbook, *Earthen Bound*, was published by Red Bird Chapbooks in February 2019. Her poem "Wild Honey Has the

Scent of Freedom" was awarded 2nd Prize in the 2017 Basil Bunting International Poetry Prize, and she has twice been a finalist for the Vallum Poetry Prize. Her poems have been nominated for Best of the Net, the Pushcart Prize, and two Illinois Arts Council Literary Awards. Currently, Lisa serves as a Poetry Editor for *Quiddity International Literary Journal*. Her reviews and interviews can be found at the *Poetry Foundation*, *Kenyon Review Online*, and the *Adroit Journal*.

Originally from Chisinau, Moldova, **Romana Iorga** lives in Switzerland. She is the author of two poetry collections in Romanian. Her work in English has appeared or is forthcoming in *Cordite Poetry Review*, *Lunch Ticket*, *American Literary Review*, *Poetry South*, *Eco-Theo Review*, *Harpur Palate*, *PANK*, and others.

Marc Jampole wrote *Music from Words* (Bellday Books, 2007) and *Cubist States of Mind/Not the Cruelest Month* (Poet's Haven Press, 2017). His poetry has appeared in many journals and anthologies. About 1,800 freelance articles he has written have been published. A former television reporter and public relations executive, Marc writes the OpEdge blog, which appears on the websites of three national publications. He is president of the board of *Jewish Currents*, a national magazine of politics and arts.

John P. Kristofco has published over seven hundred poems and seventy short stories in about two hundred different publications, including: *Folio*, *Rattle*, *Bryant Literary Review*, *Cimarron Review*, *Fourth River*, *Stand*, *The MacGuffin*, *Sierra Nevada Review*, *Blueline*, *Slant*, *Snowy Egret*, and *Clackamas Literary Review*. He has published three collections of poetry (most recently *The Timekeeper's Garden* from The Orchard Street Press) with a fourth soon to go to print. He is currently putting together a book of short stories. Jack lives with his wife Kathy in Highland Heights, Ohio.

David Langlinais has published stories in numerous journals, including *South Dakota Review, Los Angeles Review, The MacGuffin, Deep South Magazine, Avalon Literary Review,* and *Raleigh Review.* His second story collection *What Happened to All the Dogs?* (UL-Lafayette Press) came out last year. He currently lives in Dallas with his wife and daughter where he works as a freelance writer.

Jeffrey Letterly is a composer and multi-disciplined performer. He was born and raised in the heartland of the Midwest and now resides in Syracuse, NY. He has recently rekindled his interest in the unlimited capabilities of words.

Sherri Levine's poetry and other writing have appeared in *CALYX, Clackamas Literary Review, Driftwood Press, The Opiate, Sun Magazine, Timberline Review, Verseweavers,* and other publications. Levine received the 2019 Lois Cranston Memorial Poetry Prize and was awarded 1st Place in the 2017 Oregon Poetry Association's Fall Contest. She founded and hosts Head for the Hills, a monthly poetry series, which features two poets followed by an open mic. Levine's art is published in magazines and is on display at literary and art festivals. Her book, *In These Voices,* was published in 2018, by Poetry Box. She escaped the harsh weather of upstate New York and has ever since been soaking in the Oregon rain.

Jennifer Lothrigel is a poet and artist in the San Francisco Bay area. She is the author of the chapbook *Pneuma* (Liquid Light Press, 2018). Her work has also been published recently in *Phoebe Journal, Arcturus, Yes Poetry, Dash Literary Journal*, and *Adanna Journal*, among others.

Michael Milburn teaches English in New Haven, Connecticut. His poems have most recently appeared in *Mudlark* and *Antigonish Review*.

Susannah B. Mintz is a professor of English at Skidmore College. She has published extensively as a writer of creative nonfiction, with essays in *American Literary Review, The Writer's Chronicle, Epiphany, Ninth Letter, Michigan Quarterly Review*, and elsewhere. She was the winner of the 2014 South Loop National Essay Prize and a finalist for the 2010 William Allen nonfiction prize, the Epiphany chapbook contest in 2015, and the 2019 Cagibi essay prize. Her work has received special mention from Best American Essays 2010 and the Pushcart Prize Anthology 2018. A short memoir titled *Match Dot Comedy* appeared as a Kindle Single in 2013. A specialist in disability studies and scholar of autobiography, she is also the author of four monographs, most recently *The Disabled Detective: Sleuthing Disability in Contemporary Crime Fiction* (2019), in addition to numerous articles and chapters. She is also co-editor of three critical volumes. Current projects include a collection of personal essays called *Love Affair in the Garden of Milton*.

Cecil Morris retired after 37 years of teaching high school English, and now he tries writing himself what he spent so many years teaching others to understand and enjoy. He likes ice cream too much and cruciferous vegetables too little; enjoys the poetry of Sharon Olds, Tony Hoagland, Morgan Parker, and Terrance Hayes; and spends his days thinking of grandchildren. He has had a handful of poems published in *English Journal*, *The Ekphrastic Review*, *Poem*, *Dime Show Review*, *Gravel*, *The American Scholar*, and other literary magazines.

Greg Nicholl is a freelance editor whose poetry has appeared in *Crab Orchard Review*, *Ecotone*, *Mid-American Review*, *Nimrod*, *North American Review*, *Post Road*, *Prairie Schooner*, *Smartish Pace*, and elsewhere. He is a four-time Pushcart Prize nominee and currently lives in Boston.

James B. Nicola's poems have appeared stateside in *CLR*; *the Antioch*, *Southwest*, and *Atlanta Reviews*; *Rattle*; *Barrow Street*; *Tar River*; *Poetry East*; and many journals in Canada and Europe. He has been the Featured Poet in *Westward Quarterly*, *New Formalist*, and *Listening Eye*. A Yale graduate, he won a Dana Literary Award, two Willow Review awards, a People's Choice award (from Storyteller), and six Pushcart nominations—from *Shot Glass Journal*, *Parody*, *Ovunque Siamo*, *Lowestoft Chronicle*, and twice from *Trinacria*—for which he feels both stunned and grateful. His nonfiction book *Playing the Audience* won a Choice award. His poetry collections are *Manhattan Plaza* (2014), *Stage to Page: Poems from the Theater* (2016), *Wind in the Cave* (2017), *Out of Nothing: Poems of Art and Artists* (2018), and *Quickening: Poems from Before and Beyond* (2019). Currently, he hosts the Hell's Kitchen International Writers' Roundtable at Manhattan's Columbus Library.

Nancy Nowak's poetry has appeared most recently in *RAIN Magazine*, *The Timberline Review*, and *Last Call: The Anthology of Beer, Wine, & Spirits Poetry*, and was a finalist for the 2018 Letheon Prize. She has work forthcoming in *The Jefferson Journal*. From 1994 to 2016, she was an Associate Professor of Humanities at Umpqua Community College, Oregon.

Simon Perchik is an attorney whose poetry has appeared in *Partisan Review*, *The Nation*, *The New Yorker*, and elsewhere.

Paulann Petersen, Oregon Poet Laureate Emerita, has seven books of poetry, most recently *One Small Sun*, from Salmon Poetry of Ireland. The American Library Association's Booklist calls *One Small Sun* "a veritable master class in the interweaving of metaphor and memory."

Vivienne Popperl lives in Portland, Oregon. Her poetry has appeared in *RAIN Magazine*, *VoiceCatcher*, an online journal of women's voices and vision, *The Poeming Pigeon*, *Persimmon Tree Journal*, *Oyster River Pages*, and *Willawaw Journal*, and is forthcoming in *Cirque*, a Literary Journal for the North Pacific Rim. She was honored to serve as a poetry co-editor for the Fall 2017 edition of *VoiceCatcher* magazine.

Corey S. Pressman is a writer, artist, and teacher living in Portland, Oregon. He has published poetry, academic chapters, and short stories. Corey works with individuals and organizations to enable purposeful decision-making. He also regularly teaches cooking. Corey is currently Director of the Lifefinding Program at the Wayfinding Academy.

Joel Savishinsky is a retired professor of anthropology and gerontology. His books include *The Trail of the Hare: Environment and Stress in a Sub-Arctic Community*, and *Breaking The Watch: The Meanings of Retirement in America*, which won the Gerontological Society of America's book of the year prize. His poetry has appeared in *Anthropology and Humanism Quarterly, As You Were, The Avocet, The Berkshire Review, Blood and Thunder, Cirque, Crosscurrents, From Whispers to Roars, Muddy River Poetry Review, The New York Times, PageBoy, The Pharos, Passager, Shot Glass Journal, Starfish, Third Eye, Windfall,* and *Xanadu.* He lives in Seattle, helping to raise five grandchildren, and considers himself a recovering academic and unrepentant activist.

Alicia Schmidt is a punk-loving chaos pixie living in Portland, Oregon, with her family and her dog Milo. She is an avid reader and writer, and a passionate musician and vocalist in her band. She is also a feminist and social justice advocate. Her deep abiding love of all things punk and emo culture colors everything she does (black mostly). She is currently studying at Portland State University to become an English teacher.

Dave Seter is a civil engineer and poet. He writes about social and environmental issues, including the intersection of the built world and the natural world. Born in Chicago, he lives in Sonoma County, California. He earned his undergraduate degree from Princeton University and his graduate degree from Dominican University of California, where he studied ecopoetics. His full-length collection *Don't Sing to Me of Electric Fences* will be published by Cherry Grove Collections in 2021.

Chet Skibinski is a retired English teacher who has been writing for over fifty years. After a near-fatal bout with lymphoma, he published a memoir, *Cancer Country*, and he continues to enjoy writing short fiction. He lives with his wife, Linda, in Lake Oswego, Oregon.

Darcy Smith works as a sign language interpreter. Her poems have appeared and are forthcoming in *Poetry Distillery*, *ArtAscent*, *New Reader Magazine*, *Sequestrum*, *Coe Review*, and *Two Thirds North*. Darcy is a Buddhist and a kickboxer. Her current obsession is executing a six punch three kick combination with perfect form.

David Spiering writes and publishes poetry and fiction with bend toward lyrical prose. He's been a university instructor, a line cook, a natural foods and produce stocker, but he never forgets where his slippers are parked. His latest book, *My Father's Gloves*, is out from Sol books.

Matthew J. Spireng's 2019 Sinclair Prize-winning book *Good Work* is forthcoming from Evening Street Press. A 10-time Pushcart Prize nominee, he is the author of two other full-length poetry books, *What Focus Is* and *Out of Body*, winner of the 2004 Bluestem Poetry Award, and five chapbooks.

Elizabeth Stoessl lives, writes, and pays attention in Portland, Oregon, where she relocated from the East Coast and a career in public libraries. Her poetry has been published in many journals and anthologies, including *Measure*, *Passager*, *Poetica*, *The Sow's Ear Poetry Review*, *San Pedro River Review*, *VoiceCatcher*, and *Fire and Rain: Ecopoetry of California*.

John Struloeff is the author of *The Man I Was Supposed to Be* (Loom Press) and has published poems in *The Atlantic, The Southern Review, Prairie Schooner, ZYZZYVA, PN Review,* and elsewhere. He is a former Stegner and NEA Fellow and now directs the creative writing program at Pepperdine University.

Adam Tavel's third poetry collection, *Catafalque,* won the Richard Wilbur Award (University of Evansville Press, 2018).

Jacob D. Thompson was born and raised in Oregon. He is a natural storyteller and entertainer. Jacob is a film and theater student at Clackamas Community College in Oregon City, Oregon, and is pursuing his dream of being a filmmaker. Family is important to Jacob. He didn't have the most stable family growing up, but "If it weren't for family," he says, "I'd have nothing to write about." He wants to thank the teachers and instructors at Arts and Technology High school who taught him how to be a better student, writer, and person.

Marty Walsh lives in Winterport, ME. His poetry has appeared in numerous journals and reviews. Among them, *Poem* and *Cloudbank*. He is the author of *Furniture Out In The Woods* and is currently working on a second collection of poetry.

John Sibley Williams is the author of *As One Fire Consumes Another* (Orison Poetry Prize, 2019), *Skin Memory* (Backwaters Prize, University of Nebraska Press, 2019), *Summon* (JuxtaProse Chapbook Prize, 2019), *Disinheritance,* and *Controlled Hallucinations.* A twenty three-time Pushcart nominee, John is the winner of numerous awards, including the Wabash Prize for Poetry, Philip Booth Award, Phyllis

Smart-Young Prize, and Laux/Millar Prize. He serves as editor of *The Inflectionist Review* and works as a freelance poetry editor and literary agent. Previous publishing credits include: *Yale Review, North American Review, Midwest Quarterly, Southern Review, Sycamore Review, Prairie Schooner, Saranac Review, Atlanta Review, TriQuarterly*, and various anthologies.

Henry Wise is a graduate of the University of Mississippi MFA program in Poetry and the Virginia Military Institute, where he now teaches. His poems have previously appeared in *Shenandoah, Radar Poetry*, and *Nixes Mate Review*, among other journals. He lived and taught in Taiwan for several years.

The *Clackamas Literary Review* is typeset in Sabon LT Std, an old-style serif designed by Jan Tschichold, and in Optima, a humanistic sans-serif designed by Hermann Zapf, and printed on 50 lb. creme paper. Editing and design done by English Department students and faculty at Clackamas Community College, in Oregon City, Oregon.

Visit

clackamasliteraryreview.org
clackamasliteraryreview.submittable.com
facebook.com/clackamasliteraryreview
@clackamaslitrev

Contact
clr@clackamas.edu

CLACKAMAS LITERARY REVIEW

the finest writing for the best readers

Clackamas Literary Review has been committed to publishing quality writing from around the world since 1997. Use the form below or visit us on Submittable to receive the latest and forthcoming issues.

Clackamas Literary Review

_____	1 year	$12
_____	2 years	$22
_____	3 years	$32

Name _____

Address _____

City / State / Zip _____

Email _____

Send this form and check or money order to:

Clackamas Literary Review
English Department
Clackamas Community College
19600 Molalla Avenue
Oregon City, Oregon 97045